# The Numeracy File

by Mike Askew and Sheila Ebbutt

Selected articles from Junior Education magazine
on teaching and managing the National Numeracy Strategy

Published by BEAM Education
Maze Workshops
72a Southgate Road
London N1 3JT

British Library Cataloguing-in-Publication Data
A catalogue record for this publication is available from the British Library

ISBN 1 903142 04 0

Cover illustration © Ali Pellatt
Main illustrations © Spike Gerrell
Diagram illustrations on pages 12, 14 and 60 © Andy Martin
Printed in England by the Drakeford Press

# Contents

Introduction     5

Section 1
Key elements of the *Framework for Teaching Mathematics*     7

Section 2
Managing the Daily Mathematics Lesson     35

Sample lessons
(Year 3 to Year 6)     58

About the authors     64

*This book is dedicated to Billie Old*

# Introduction

by Terry Saunders of Junior Education Magazine

As soon as the Government announced that it was introducing a Numeracy Strategy, complete with daily maths lessons, into all primary schools in England, I telephoned Sheila Ebbutt at BEAM. Junior Education's valued relationship with junior school teachers, and its reputation for responding rapidly to curricular changes on their behalf, meant that I needed the best possible translation of how the new requirements would impact on them. I wanted to be able to offer, very quickly, an interpretation of how those requirements could be turned into stimulating, innovative and effective classroom practice. Sheila was already well-known to Junior Ed – and she didn't let me down!

Because the National Numeracy Strategy is a complete programme with a clearly defined structure and framework, the way that mathematics was taught in almost all junior schools had to change. What I needed was a series of articles that would help teachers cope with such a major upheaval. The series would have to concentrate on the most important aspects of the new Numeracy Strategy – and would have to dovetail, month by month, into a comprehensive classroom manual. It would also have to offer a watertight guarantee: to provide teachers with the enthusiasm, inspiration and mathematical expertise to turn the Numeracy Strategy into effective, high-quality teaching practice. Sheila readily agreed to write those articles for us,

together with BEAM colleague Mike Askew – and this book, based on that series, is the culmination of their efforts.

The timing of the Government's announcement meant that we were able to set the scene with our articles twelve months before the Strategy was scheduled to start in our classrooms, thereby helping teachers to get to grips with what they were expected to do without the usual rush which characterises so many of the Government's new initiatives.

We wanted to demonstrate to teachers how they could plan, organise, manage and introduce the daily mathematics lesson; how they could incorporate the new emphasis on mental mathematics into their lessons; how they could successfully implement the new range of teaching approaches required by the Strategy; how they could help children to acquire key mathematical skills and working methods and how they could cover particular issues such as differentiation, special needs, additional adult helpers and mathematics resources.

We were delighted with the success of the articles – and many teachers have already made the effort to let us know how we helped them to survive the National Numeracy Strategy. I know that this book will do the same for you!

# Section 1

## Key elements of the
## *Framework for Teaching Mathematics*

| | |
|---|---|
| What is numeracy? | 8 |
| Place value | 10 |
| Fractions | 12 |
| Ratio and proportion | 14 |
| Addition and subtraction | 16 |
| Multiplication and division | 18 |
| Figuring out | 20 |
| Paper and pencil methods | 22 |
| More on intermediate recording | 24 |
| Towards formal recording | 26 |
| Mathematical problems | 28 |
| Starting with problems | 30 |
| Children inventing problems | 32 |

# What is numeracy?

Numeracy is at the heart of the Government's strategy to improve mathematics standards. But what *is* numeracy – and how does the strategy's approach impact on teachers and children?

## What is numeracy?

*'Numeracy at Key Stages 1 and 2 is a proficiency and confidence with number and measures. It requires an understanding of our number system, a repertoire of computational skills, and an inclination and ability to solve number problems in a variety of contexts. Numeracy also demands practical understanding of the ways in which information is gathered by counting and measuring, and is presented in graphs, diagrams, charts and tables. This proficiency is promoted through giving sharper focus to the relevant aspects of the National Curriculum programmes of study for mathematics. Numerate pupils should be confident and competent enough to tackle problems without going immediately to teachers and friends for help.'*
The Numeracy Task Force: Final Report

## The numeracy 'hour'

The Numeracy Task Force identified as a key objective that all children have a daily mathematics lesson of 45 to 60 minutes or more with good quality teaching. They recommended that children spend a high proportion of time in these lessons being taught as a class. Good direct teaching was defined in terms of a daily lesson that:

– *'gives children instruction and demonstrates, explains and illustrates mathematics, setting the work in different contexts and linking it to previous work'*

– *'maximises the opportunities for the teacher to interact with pupils, so that they can talk and be listened to, and receive feedback that helps them to develop their mathematical knowledge, skills and understanding' and*

– *'allows pupils to show what they know, explain their thinking and methods, and suggest alternative ways of tackling problems'*

The Numeracy Task Force's definition of numeracy at primary level highlighted a range of key skills, abilities and areas of knowledge.

Numerate pupils should:

*'Have a sense of the size of a number and where it fits into the number system'*
Children should develop a clear understanding of place value and the number system by using number lines, cards and grids such as a 100-grid in group games and activities and in class discussions. For example, look with the class at the effect of counting in tens, using a 100-grid.

*'Know by heart number facts such as number bonds, multiplication tables, division facts, doubles and halves'*
Daily mathematics lessons should be used to help children develop a repertoire of computational skills, through whole-class activities involving work on mental calculations and strategies. This means developing quick games at the beginnings and ends of lessons to reinforce children's knowledge.

*'Use what they know by heart to figure out answers mentally'*
Children should be helped to use number facts that they know to derive new ones. Children can't learn and remember every number fact, but they need to be able to do quick and efficient mental calculations. This means being able to use what they know – for example, working out 25 + 27 by remembering that double 25 is 50, then adding on 2.

*'Calculate accurately and efficiently, both mentally and on paper, drawing on a range of calculation strategies'*
Children need to practise and use the mathematics they know in a range of situations. They should

> Children need experience of solving problems where they have to check their calculations

talk about how they work on problems and learn from each other as well as from the teacher. They should use written methods to support their mental methods, and talk about these too. They should compare methods and learn to discern more efficient ways of calculating. They should also learn how to check their work for accuracy.

*'Recognise when it is appropriate to use a calculator – and when it is not – and be able to use one effectively'*
Contrary to items in the newspapers, there is no ban on the use of calculators in primary schools. But the Numeracy Task Force emphasised that we should teach children effective ways of using calculators, and use them to encourage mathematical thinking. Calculators should not be used for simple arithmetic.

*'Make sense of number problems, including non-routine problems, and recognise the operations needed to solve them'*
Children need a lot of experience of unravelling problems before they can confidently tackle them alone. Talk through word problems and invite children to discuss what the words mean and what calculation methods to use. Present calculations in a wide variety of contexts, where it is not immediately obvious what operations are involved.

*'Explain their methods and reasoning using correct mathematical terms; judge whether their answers are reasonable, and have strategies for checking them where necessary'*
The National Numeracy Strategy published their book of mathematical vocabulary to support the teaching of correct mathematical terminology. This involves talking about mathematics with children and producing definitions through discussion and demonstration.

It is also through discussion that children learn how to decide whether the results of calculations are reasonable. Children need experience of solving problems where they cannot judge the results intuitively but have to check their calculations – for example, problems such as 'How much paper does the class use in a day?' or 'Would you rather have your height in £1 coins or your weight in 2p pieces?'.

*'Suggest suitable units for measuring, and make sensible estimates of measurements'*
Obviously, before they can learn to make sensible estimates, children need plenty of experience of measuring. They also need to use graduated scales on different measuring tools, and to discuss how to use the tools and how to read the scales.

*'Explain and make predictions from the numbers in graphs, diagrams, charts and tables'*
When working on data handling, it is important to use situations and data that are familiar to the children. For example, children can carry out a survey on how the playground is used, collecting statistical information about this, creating tables and charts, and making recommendations about how to improve playground use. In addition to this first-hand experience, newspapers, posters, leaflets and other media all show a range of ways of presenting information. We should try to give children experience of these different representations, and help them learn how to interpret them through discussion. ∎

Numerate pupils tackle problems with confidence and competence

# Place value

Place value lies at the heart of our number system. But do we need to modify our traditional approach to teaching this important concept?

In our number system there are just ten digits: 0, 1, 2, 3, 4, 5, 6, 7, 8, and 9. We can write any number by using digits from 1 to 9 in different positions and by using zero to 'hold the place' when no digit is required. For example, we can represent one hundred and one as 101. As there are three digits we know that the left-hand 1 represents one hundred, the zero shows that there are no tens and the right-hand 1 represents just one. This powerful technique has allowed the development of modern mathematics.

The Hindus were the first people to use a representation for zero in this way, eliminating the need for symbols of numbers greater than nine. This number system was picked up and developed by Arab traders in the 9th century and spread to Europe, but it was not widely used in England until the 18th century because the Church thought that knowledge of such mathematics would give ordinary people too much power!

## The teaching of place value

Place value is a powerful mathematical tool but it is also very abstract. During the past 30 years primary teachers have tried hard to teach it – but they have not always been successful. Our spoken English language does not help because its written and spoken number words do not support what happens with actual numbers. The place value notation is regular but the spoken pattern with smaller numbers is not. In some languages, the pattern goes: 'one, two, three, four, five, six, seven, eight, nine, one-ty, one-ty one, one-ty two, one-ty three, one-ty four... In English we have the anomalous '...ten, eleven, twelve, thirteen, fourteen...'

Once you count beyond 20, and continue over 100, the pattern becomes clearer. You still have to deal with the irregular tens numbers: 'twenty' instead of 'two-ty, 'thirty' instead of 'three-ty' but the numbers become regular from 60. One mistake has been to keep children working with small numbers – irregularly named numbers – until they are ready for larger numbers. But if they encountered large numbers sooner, it would lead to a better understanding.

*Place value is a powerful tool – but it is also very abstract*

Over the past few decades it was considered important to give children practical and physical experience of the size of numbers – notably with the use of base-ten materials such as Dienes' apparatus. Current thinking is that this is not particularly helpful. The structure of the number system is about how digits are used to represent numbers – not about the number of objects the numbers might represent. Place value work should focus on the structure of the system which ordains how the digits are set out rather than diverting attention to objects. Alongside this, more attention should be paid to the ordering of numbers. So 57 might be thought of as 50 + 7 or 55 + 2 or 60 – 3.

## Exploring place value mentally

The traditional approach to setting out calculations vertically is also unhelpful. When children are given a calculation such as:

$$57$$
$$+ \, 34$$
$$\overline{\phantom{00}}$$

they are generally asked to work from the right; they will say 'Seven and four is eleven, put down one and carry one. Five and three is eight and one more is nine'. They have treated all the numbers as units digits. They end up with an answer of 91, but conceptually it is a nine and a one.

However, if you ask children to tackle '57 plus 34' mentally, most of them will automatically start with the tens, 'fifty and thirty is eighty', then deal with the units and adjust the tens, or, more usefully, keep the 57 whole, add on 30 then add on 4. This is the kind of strategy we want to encourage them to use.

Working out difficult calculations by laying them out vertically is sometimes efficient – but not always. We should present problems to children in a variety of formats: orally, setting them out horizontally, as written word problems or in puzzle form. They then have a choice about how to solve each problem as it arises –

and they can use their knowledge of place value.

Even when calculations are presented vertically children should be encouraged to ask themselves whether they have the confidence to work out the answer mentally.

## A visual approach to numbers

The mathematician Caleb Gattegno developed a way to help children link place value notation visually and aurally with a chart showing the structure of the place value system.

The chart can be used to help children associate the language of the numbers with the underlying patterns. You can:

– say a number, such as 'five hundred and thirty seven', and point to each part of the number on the chart as you say it

| 1000 | 2000 | 3000 | 4000 | 5000 | 6000 | 7000 | 8000 | 9000 |
|------|------|------|------|------|------|------|------|------|
| 100  | 200  | 300  | 400  | 500  | 600  | 700  | 800  | 900  |
| 10   | 20   | 30   | 40   | 50   | 60   | 70   | 80   | 90   |
| 1    | 2    | 3    | 4    | 5    | 6    | 7    | 8    | 9    |

– point out or 'tap' out a number and ask the children to say that number

– ask children to tap out a number as you say it

– look at numbers such as nine hundred and eight, where there are no tens

– ask children to tap out the number ten more than 564, or the number 100 less than 752

– ask children to work individually on the same activities using place value arrow cards:

For example, they can show how 'five hundred and thirty seven' is made up by building up the numbers with the cards. ■

We can write any number using digits 1 to 9, using zero to 'hold the place'

# Fractions

Fractions can be a tricky concept for children to grasp – and it is important that we give them the time and practice they need to move from decimals to percentages with relative ease.

## The difficulties children have with fractions

Young children are able to use numbers as adjectives and can answer questions like 'What are two elephants and two elephants?' But it takes time and experience for them to deal with two as an abstract idea in its own right and tell you that two plus two is four. The abstractions involved in fractions are even more complex and we should not expect children to grasp them quickly or easily.

Part of the difficulty children have with fractions stems from the variety of ways that they are used. For example, $\frac{3}{4}$ can mean:

– a part of a 'whole', found by dividing the whole into four equal parts and taking three of them

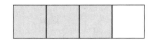

– a comparison between a set of objects and part of the set – 'three quarters of the dots are blue'

– a point on a number line lying between two whole numbers

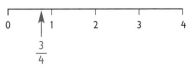

– the result of a division – 'How much chocolate does each person get if three bars are divided amongst four people?'

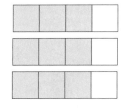

– a comparison between the sizes of two sets of objects or two measurements – 'A has $\frac{3}{4}$ as many dots as B' or 'snake B is $\frac{3}{4}$ of the length of snake A'

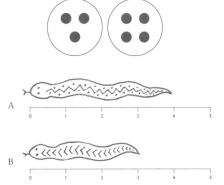

*We should not expect children to grasp fractions quickly or easily*

Decimal fractions or percentages can also be interpreted in each of these ways. Is it any wonder that teaching and learning fractions is so notoriously difficult?

## Which model to introduce first?

*Parts of a whole*
Children are generally introduced to fractions as parts of a whole (the first kind listed above). This is often regarded as the easiest model. But even something as seemingly simple as the idea of a half is not obvious for all children. Research shows that there are 12- and 13-year-olds who think that the circle on the right has been split into two halves, possibly as a result of everyday experiences where you can be offered the 'bigger half'.

*Whole set and part set*
Another difficulty children sometimes have is grasping the idea of fractions greater than one unit. When asked what fraction is represented by the diagram below, many children will say $\frac{7}{10}$ rather than $\frac{7}{5}$ or $1\frac{2}{5}$. Exploring

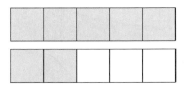

fractions in the 'sets' model (second in the list above) may help children to understand that fractions can have values greater than one. But other misunderstandings can occur with this model. Work by the Assessment of Performance Unit in the 1980s found that almost a third of 11-year-olds, when given four squares, three blue and one red, thought that a third of the squares were red rather than a quarter.

*A number on a line*

The 'number line' model of fractions links with children's experience of reading scales on rulers, thermometers and so on. Marking fractions on a number line can help with the idea of fractions as numbers in their own right – but because this is more abstract than the previous models, it is important to help children to decide what the unit is. For example, asked to mark $\frac{3}{5}$ on the line below, children may point to 3, having interpreted the

task as having to mark a point $\frac{3}{5}$ of the way along the whole line.

## Some useful tips

As outlined above, children can have all kinds of problems and misconceptions when working with fractions. Here are a few tips to make life easier for you and for them:

*Give children plenty of experiences with all the different fraction models*

The wider children's experience of fractional concepts, the more opportunities they have to assemble their ideas in some coherent kind of way, and get an overview of the whole area of fractions. So don't stick to one of the models listed above, but work with two, three or more of them.

*Always emphasise 'a fraction of what?'*

It is important to discuss with the children exactly what they are finding a fraction of. 'Three quarters of what?' should be a frequently asked question, with answers such as, 'three quarters of the square', 'three quarters of 20' or 'three quarters of the distance between 0 and 1'.

*Talk, talk, talk*

Ask the children to discuss their ideas about fractions with you and with each other. Have group discussions, class discussions, discussions in pairs. Ask them to share their ideas, and challenge each other, arguing about how to visualise problems and how to tackle them. The more they verbalise what is going on in their heads the more clarity they will get about their own ideas, and the better the chances that misconceptions will be picked up. ■

> The more children verbalise what is going on in their heads, the more clarity they will get about their own ideas

# Ratio and proportion

Ratio and proportion are now part of the primary mathematics curriculum – and the best way to make sure they don't cause difficulties is to get the language right.

What fraction is represented by the black sheep?

Two fifths is one answer. But is it the only possible answer? In fact, 'two fifths' is the answer to: 'What proportion of the group of sheep is black?'

'Two fifths' is not a statement about the black sheep in themselves but a statement about the black sheep compared with something else. We just take it as read that the comparison is with the whole group.

Many children will answer 'two thirds' when asked what fraction the black sheep represent. They compare the black sheep with the white sheep, answering instead the question: 'What is the ratio of black sheep to white sheep?'

## New to the primary curriculum

'One for me, four for the pot, one for me, four for the pot.' Anyone who has ever been berry picking and gone home with juice on their face has experienced the roots of proportion and ratio. Traditionally part of the secondary mathematics curriculum, proportion and ratio has been introduced by the *Framework for Teaching Mathematics* into the primary mathematics curriculum as part of fractions. The aim of this is to lay the foundations for work on scaling and other aspects of secondary mathematics. At primary level, however, the emphasis is on making sense of situations rather than the application of a mathematical formula – that can come much later.

As with many areas of mathematics, using the correct vocabulary is vital to children's understanding of proportion and ratio. Only when children are confident with the language of proportion – 'in every' – and ratio – 'for every' – should they begin to explore simple problem-solving situations. In devising

*The emphasis is on making sense of situations, not applying a mathematical formula*

problems for the children to work on, it is best to take one situation and develop several related problems.

## The language of proportion

Proportion is about comparing a part of a whole with the whole. Our everyday lives are peppered with talk of proportion – 'Four out of every five cats prefer Tibby'; 'The proportion of four-year-olds in reception classes is increasing'; 'What proportion of the country wears glasses?' Implicit in such statements is the language of 'in every' – 'one in every five digits is a thumb'; 'one in every five adults has a form of disability'.

Also implicit when talking about proportion is some form of a total. Sometimes, this is deliberately obscure – four out of five dentists recommended 'Dent-u-white'. Is this four fifths of all dentists in the country, four fifths of a random sample of 100, or four out of five particular dentists invited to comment? Having a sense of proportion is part of being fully numerate.

## Using pattern strips

In the diagram above, one in every four squares is shaded. Working with such diagrams not only helps children to develop the language of the proportion, it can also help their understanding of equivalence of fractions. Ask the children to

## Percentages

Percentages are just one particular form of proportion – how many in every 100? Pattern strips can help children develop images of this: ask them to imagine how many squares would be shaded if the strips were 100 squares long.

## The language of ratio

While proportion is about comparing a part with a whole, ratio is about comparing two separate parts. We have five digits on each of our hands, one of which is a thumb. The proportion of digits that are thumbs is $\frac{1}{5}$ – one in every five digits is a thumb. But another way of considering thumbs is in relation to fingers: the ratio of thumbs to fingers is one in four or $\frac{1}{4}$. There is one thumb for every four fingers: 'for every' is the language of ratio.

*'In every' or 'for every'?*
Children will need a lot of time to talk about the difference between 'in every' and 'for every'. Use simple examples and build on their intuitive understanding of proportion – focusing on the differences between ratio and proportion and on the language involved. For example, berry picking can be talked about in both ways. Suppose you pick four berries at a time and eat one berry in every four (or one 'out of every four' as we commonly say – yet more cause for confusion). Comparing the number of berries eaten with the number picked – a part-whole comparison, a proportion – you eat one in four, or $\frac{1}{4}$.

Alternatively, you can compare the number eaten with the number in the basket – a part-part comparison, a ratio. If you eat one in every four picked that means you eat one and take three home; the ratio of berries eaten to berries taken home is one for every three, 1:3. ■

imagine the same pattern but in different lengths – this can help them to appreciate the basic invariance of proportion – one in four squares is shaded, whatever the size of the whole.

Show the strip pattern to children and say, "Suppose I had lots of strips like this, all 20 squares long". Now ask questions which draw on ideas of both proportion and fractions, such as:

- How many shaded squares are there in every 20 squares? (Five in every 20, or one in every four.) What fraction of the 20 squares would be shaded? ($\frac{5}{20}$ or $\frac{1}{4}$)

- Suppose the strips are 40 squares long. How many shaded squares are there in every 40 squares? (Ten in every 40, or one in every four.) What fraction of the squares is shaded? ($\frac{10}{40}$ or $\frac{1}{4}$)

- What if the strips were 100 squares long? ($\frac{25}{100}$ or $\frac{1}{4}$)

- Or 1000 squares long? ($\frac{250}{1000}$ or $\frac{1}{4}$)

Whatever the length of the strip, the fraction of shaded squares is always one quarter!

Talk about the difference between 'in every' and 'for every'

# Addition and subtraction

Mental mathematics is the linchpin of the Numeracy Strategy – and children need a range of key skills that will allow them to perform mental addition and subtraction calculations with confidence.

At the end of Year 2, children are expected to:

- know by heart addition and subtraction facts to 10

- be able to find a small difference by counting up from the smaller to the larger number

- add or subtract 9 or 11 by adding or subtracting 10 and adjusting

- identify near doubles

Children are expected to make a lot of progress in addition and subtraction during Key Stage 2. They need to gain a firm understanding of how numbers work. In addition and subtraction the important areas are:

**commutativity**
that 46 + 37 = 37 + 46

**associativity**
that (46+37) + 5 = 46 + (37 + 5)

**inverses**
that addition undoes subtraction and subtraction undoes addition

**zero**
that adding and subtracting zero makes no difference

**subtraction**
that you can use addition to solve a subtraction problem

*Children need to be able to say what they think without fear of being squashed*

**using number bonds**
that you can add multiples of tens in the same way as you add numbers to 10, so 30 + 40 is similar to 3 + 4; if you know 3 + 4 = 7, you know that 30 + 40 = 70.

If they achieve as expected, by the end of Year 6 they will be able to add mentally numbers such as 470 + 380; add and subtract decimals; and use written methods to add or subtract any two numbers. That's a lot to get through in four years!

## How to get there

Practising pages of sums in exercise books does not produce the understanding or fluency needed to achieve the Year 6 goals. The key is to develop mental calculation methods. When children calculate with numbers in their heads they make connections that give them a deeper understanding of how the number system works. They gain confidence in working with numbers, and they find their own calculation short cuts. Using numbers mentally gives children a greater feel for problem solving and for choosing appropriate

calculations in real life problems. It also helps them to understand how written methods work and when they should be used.

## What are mental calculations?

There are two aspects to mental calculations: knowing by heart, and being able to calculate quickly. By Year 3, children should know by heart number bonds to 10, including doubles, and be very familiar with number bonds to 20. That's all they need to recall instantly. To calculate quickly and efficiently they need to know how to use these facts, how the number system works, and how to derive new facts from the ones they know. Knowing by heart is the easiest bit; short bouts of daily practice will achieve this. The main work is in helping children to understand the logic and order behind numbers, and to develop strategies for manoeuvring them in their heads.

## Encouraging mental maths

We need to encourage children to do as much mental calculation as possible, and to write down only what cannot be comfortably held in the head – this is how most adults operate. Given the mental addition or subtraction of two two-digit numbers, most adults and children work from left to right – they deal with the tens first, then the units, and then adjust as necessary. The written vertical presentation of the same calculation implies that you deal

with the units first and then the tens – a method that is not efficient if carried out mentally. It also discourages you from thinking of the numbers as two-digit numbers and from making a rough estimate of the total.

## Ways of adding and subtracting mentally

The methods below involve using what you know to figure out new facts. These are the kinds of mental methods we can introduce to children. Each method can also be used with subtractions.

$$46 + 37 = ?$$

*Method 1*
Split the numbers into tens and deal with these first:

- Add 40 and 30 to make 70

- That leaves 6 and 7 to add on

- Split the 7 into 4 and 3, using the 4 to make the 6 up to 10

- 70 and 10 is 80

- Add the 3 left from the 7 to make 83

*Method 2*
A more efficient mental method is to split just one of the tens numbers. This removes a step from the calculation:

- Add 46 and 30 to make 76

- That leaves 7 to add on

- Split the 7 into 4 and 3

- Add the 4 to the 76 to make 80 and the 3 to make 83

*Method 3*
Another method involves compensating for an over-calculation:

- To make adding 46 and 37 easier, think of 37 as 40

- Add 46 and 40 to make 86

- Now take 3 from the 86 to compensate for making the 37 into 40. That makes 83

An empty number line is a useful image to use in describing these methods to children.

## Building confidence

Mental maths is not intended to be like mental arithmetic in the 1950s, where children were pressured into answering quick-fire questions around the class. Developing children's mental strategies with numbers involves the teacher knowing the range of methods that children might employ and building on these. It entails listening to their explanations and encouraging them to discuss their thoughts and mental processes. It means helping them to refine and develop these methods to make them more workable. And for all of this to happen, the classroom needs to be a safe place in which children can say what they are thinking without fear of being squashed, where they can introduce an idea, however off the wall, and know that it will be carefully considered by others in the room. ■

# Multiplication and division

Learning multiplication and division facts needn't be a long and laborious task. Children need a toolkit of mental strategies that they can use for both rapid recall and figuring out.

The National Numeracy Strategy separates out knowledge of multiplication and division into the number facts that children need to be able to recall rapidly and those they should be able to figure out mentally. By the end of Year 6 the majority of children should be able to recall rapidly all the multiplication facts and the corresponding division facts for the tables up to 10 × 10.

Children are expected to figure out larger calculations, using a range of mental techniques. These include:

– multiplying numbers by 10 or 100

– doubling and halving

– multiplying two-digit multiples of 10 by a single digit, for example 60 × 4

– dividing multiples of 1000 by 100 or 10, for example 7000 ÷ 10

– finding squares of multiples of 10 to 100, such as 30 squared = 900

## Tables or multiplication facts?

Learning the tables is only one part of committing multiplication and division facts to memory. While the tables are neat they have the disadvantage that they separate out the 100 multiplication facts – so 6 × 7 is separate from 7 × 6. Often children who have learned up to the six times table do not realise that they have already learned much of the seven times table from the facts in the early tables. Learning the multiplication facts strategically helps children to make connections between facts and reduces the burden on their memory.

*Learning triples*
Make sure that children are secure in their knowledge of triples – the sets of three numbers that are linked together by multiplication and division, for example 3, 8, 24. They should know that 3 × 8 = 24, 8 × 3 = 24, 24 ÷ 3 = 8; 24 ÷ 8 = 3. Help them use the following to establish these number facts.

*Commutativity*
Multiplication is commutative; this means that the order of the numbers doesn't affect the answer – for example, 3 × 4 gives the same result as 4 × 3. This immediately reduces by half the number of multiplication

Commutativity halves the number of multiplication facts that children have to remember

facts that children have to remember. To help them appreciate this, use the array model for multiplication. Here, rotating the array by 90° shows that four rows of three is the same as three rows of four.

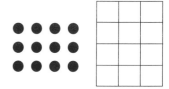

*Doubling*
Knowledge of doubles not only helps with addition. It is also crucial to committing multiplication and division facts to memory. Being able to double doesn't just give you the two times table – it also means you can remind yourself what, say, 6 × 8 comes to when you have forgotten.

Double 6: $6 \times 2 = 12$

double again: $6 \times 4 = 24$

and double once more: $6 \times 8 = 48$

If you can double, you can also multiply large numbers by 2 rapidly. For example, to do $324 \times 2$, double it to get 648.

*Multiplying by 10*
Children should know instantly how to multiply by 10 and later by 100. They might say that the short-cut method is to 'add a 0'. However, the fact that the rule does not hold for multiplying decimal numbers means it is better to point out to children from the start that multiplying by 10 makes everything ten times bigger – and so all the digits move left one place.

$$3 \rightarrow 3$$
$$30 \rightarrow 3 \times 10$$
$$300 \rightarrow 3 \times 100$$

*Counting in fives and threes*
The pattern of fives can be explored by counting on in fives and by halving multiples of 10. With the multiples of 3, there are no real short cuts to learning – children simply need to rehearse them. However, it is helpful to explore the pattern that the multiples of 3 make. Add together

Making connections between facts reduces the burden on children's memory

the digits that make up any multiple of 3 until a single digit is reached and the answer will always be 3, 6, or 9.

| 12  | 1 + 2     | 3  |            |
| 15  | 1 + 5     | 6  |            |
| 18  | 1 + 8     | 9  |            |
| 21  | 2 + 1     | 3  |            |
| 156 | 1 + 5 + 6 | 12 | 1 + 2 = 3  |
| 333 | 3 + 3 + 3 | 9  |            |

*The patterns of nines*
The multiples of 9 are even easier than the threes. Add together the digits that make up any multiple of 9 – until a single digit is reached – and the answer will always be 9.

| 18  | 1 + 8     | 9  |           |
| 27  | 2 + 7     | 9  |           |
| 36  | 3 + 6     | 9  |           |
| 45  | 4 + 5     | 9  |           |
| 54  | 5 + 4     | 9  |           |
| 63  | 6 + 3     | 9  |           |
| 99  | 9 + 9     | 18 | 1 + 8 = 9 |
| 387 | 3 + 8 + 7 | 18 | 1 + 8 = 9 |

Another way of exploring the nines pattern is to multiply by 10 and subtract the number being multiplied.
So $9 \times 4 = 40 - 4 = 36$
$9 \times 8 = 80 - 8 = 72$.
Finger multiplication for nines also appeals to children. Hold out both hands palms up and mentally label the fingers and thumbs from 1 to 10 starting at the far left. Bend towards you the finger that has the value you want to multiply by 9, for example, 7. The number of fingers to the left of the bent finger is the number of tens in the answer. The number of fingers to the right of the bent finger is the number of units in the answer. So $9 \times 7 = 63$.

*Square numbers*
The square numbers – $1 \times 1$, $2 \times 2$ up to $10 \times 10$ – are the cornerstones of the multiplication facts. If children know, say, $6 \times 6$

is 36, they can easily work out $7 \times 6$ by adding on another 6 to get 42. Work with arrays and number patterns helps children remember the square numbers.

## Combining strategies

If children are confident with these strategies, they should have no problem with the multiplication and division facts to $10 \times 10$. Combining the strategies will allow them to go beyond $10 \times 10$. Realising that doubling and doubling again is the same as multiplying by 4 makes $36 \times 4$ a reasonable mental calculation. Reversing this – halving and halving again – gives a useful strategy for $76 \div 4$. Combining doubling with multiplying by 10 makes mental multiplication by 20 possible. Figuring out $38 \times 5$ by multiplying by 10 and halving is more efficient than multiplying the 30 and 8 by 5 separately.

## Reconstructing the tables

Using these strategies, children can reconstruct forgotten tables:

| $\times 2$  | double                                    |
| $\times 3$  | count in threes                           |
| $\times 4$  | double and double again                   |
| $\times 5$  | pattern of fives or multiply by 10 and halve |
| $\times 6$  | $\times 3$ then double                    |
| $\times 9$  | pattern of nines                          |
| $\times 10$ | place value                               |

So what about the sevens and eights? Well, if children know that multiplication is commutative, they can turn around most of the 7 and 8 table facts – $7 \times 5$ becomes $5 \times 7$. Only three facts are then not covered – $7 \times 7$, $8 \times 8$ and $7 \times 8$. The first two are covered by knowing the square numbers. $7 \times 8$? Well, you just have to remember that one – it's the table fact that everyone finds most difficult! ∎

# Figuring out

Ignore pressure to conform to the socially accepted ways of figuring out the answers to calculations. Instead, develop a set of flexible approaches to numeracy that work for you.

## Cheating – or not

Graham in Year 4 was doing some simple divisions. To work out 21 divided by 3 he counted in 3s, holding out a finger for each step. When he reached 21, he looked at his fingers and wrote down 7. Further down his worksheet, he had to find the answer to 27 divided by 3. "I'm cheating on this one," he told me. "I know that 3 into 21 is 7," he went on, putting out 7 fingers. He then counted on 3 from 21 to 24, then 3 more to 27, and wrote down 9.

A group of teachers were asked whether they could figure out the remainder mentally when 1256 was divided by 6. When we talked about the methods they had used, all but one claimed to have tried to picture a written division calculation in their heads and then work it out ('6 into 1 won't go') – with varying degrees of success. The exception was a teacher called Olive, who said: "Well, I know 6 goes into 1200, so I only needed to worry about 6 into 56." At the end of the session, Olive came up to say that she had never been any good at maths and she wanted to

apologise for not having done the calculation 'in the proper way'!

We would say that Graham and Olive were both displaying highly numerate behaviours. So why are such methods often regarded as 'cheating' or 'not proper'? There seems to be a deep-rooted belief in mathematics that getting the answer is not sufficient: you have to arrive at it in a socially accepted way – and that often means the most difficult way you can think of. The general view seems to be that if it is not difficult, then it cannot really be maths!

## Looking for short cuts

Using short cuts to figure out answers is not cheating: it is part of developing a set of flexible approaches to becoming numerate. Research evidence shows that using strategies to figure things out actually helps children to commit number facts to memory: the child who initially figures out four sevens by doubling twice will, in all likelihood, come to 'know' that the answer is 28. So what short cuts can we use to figure things out? Using

'Double and double again' can be generalised to many numbers

what you know, building on previous answers, looking for 'free gifts' and transforming calculations into easier ones are all useful – and related – strategies.

*Using what you know*

My memory is cluttered up enough without carrying around excess number facts. So I cannot rapidly recall the answer to 65 multiplied by 4, and I doubt whether many of you can either. But I do know that doubling and doubling again will help me to reach the answer (260) quickly enough. Rather than expecting children to commit the 4 times table to memory straight away, we can work with them on arriving at the answers through this strategy.

The beauty of a method such as 'double and double again' is that it can easily be generalised to many numbers. Children can multiply any number by 4 by simply doubling and doubling again, or by 8 if they double once more.

*Building on previous answers*

Graham used the information from one of his answers to figure out another; but all too often, children treat each calculation as if it must be tackled from scratch. During whole-class question and answer sessions, it is helpful to build on the answers already found. So, ask Jan what 40 add 30 is then follow up by asking Sam what 40 add 29 must be. This approach not only directs children to look for connections between calculations (as in 'free gifts' below), but also encourages them to listen to the teacher's questions even when someone else is being asked to answer them.

### Looking for free gifts

Know one, get three free! Free gifts are the additional calculations that come 'free' when you know one number fact. This strategy depends on knowledge of the relationships between operations. So, if I know that $7 \times 8$ is 56, then I have the three free gifts: the answers to $8 \times 7$, $56 \div 7$ and $56 \div 8$. This is far easier than committing 'seven eights' to memory in the week that we do the seven times table, then 'eight sevens' when we do the eight times table.

### Transforming calculations

Carrying out calculations that involve numbers such as 38 or 83 is awkward in comparison to working with multiples of ten. So, encourage children to work with 'nice' numbers and adjust the answer later. For example, 56 subtract 38 is fairly easy to do mentally if you subtract 40 and then add back the extra 2 that you took away.

Similarly, to do 56 multiplied by 38, use pencil jottings to help you do 56 multiplied by 40 (easy: double, that's 112, double again, that's 224, then multiply by 10, that's 2240) then subtract double 56 (2240 subtract 112 is 2128).

## Making maths easy

All too often, children think that they must do a calculation exactly as it is set. But help them spend a moment looking for ways to transform it and life can be much easier. And, after all, don't we want children to find maths easy? ∎

# Paper and pencil methods

The *Framework for Teaching Mathematics* gives clear guidance on teaching pencil and paper strategies – and explains when it is appropriate to use them in the classroom.

A progression towards compact written methods involves recording mental methods used in a calculation until children no longer need these steps. Some children will prefer to continue using extended written methods while others will prefer shorter methods.

The Numeracy Task Force's Final Report emphasised that it is mental, not written, calculation methods that lie at the heart of numeracy. This put written work in a different perspective. It is still considered important – but the way in which children record their mathematics has been re-thought. Children's experience should encompass a range of mental calculations and written methods with a progression from one to the other.

## Framework guidance

The guidance in the National Numeracy Strategy's *Framework for Teaching Mathematics* is to leave paper and pencil methods of recording until the third term of Year 3. Before that, children are expected to use oral methods for calculation, together with objects or fingers, then number lines and grids, and informal jottings to help. This allows for emphasis to be put on mental calculation and mental recall.

When working towards written methods, introduce a range of recording methods that show how the calculation progresses in stages. For example, children can work out a problem such as: 'Billy has 53 marbles. He buys another 24. How many marbles does he have altogether?' and explain their mental methods. You could show how to solve it using an empty number line:

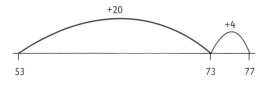

Write the same calculation vertically, making the number line method clear in the layout:

```
    53
+   24
    ──
    73  (53 + 20)
    77  (73 + 4)
```

You can then show another method, adding the tens first:

```
    53
+   24
    ──
    70  (50 + 20)
     7  (3 + 4)
    ──
    77
```

## Why use pencil and paper?

With the new emphasis on mental methods, it is necessary to rethink why we teach children to use pencil and paper for calculations.

*Jottings*
The main reason for using pencil and paper is to extend the mental screen, jotting down information that would be too much to hold in short-term memory. Part of the strategy will then be to make informal pencil and paper jottings to record interim information to help with the calculation. These notes may not make sense to anyone not involved in the lesson – but they are an important stage in developing fluency in mental mathematics.

For example, to work out 28 + 24, a child might jot down a diagram such as the one shown below and do the calculation in stages:

$$28 + 20 + 2 + 2$$

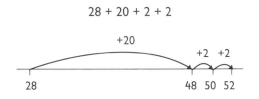

Alternatively, they might write the sum in a way that will show the stages of their thinking:

$$28 + 20 \rightarrow 48$$

$$48 + 2 \rightarrow 50$$

$$50 + 2 \rightarrow 52$$

or

$$28 \searrow 20$$
$$48 \searrow 2$$
$$50 \searrow 2$$
$$52$$

Am I confident that I can do this in my head – or do I need to make some recording?

*Informal recordings*
Recording the stages of their calculations like this encourages children to analyse and check their own thinking processes – it also shows you their methods. Informal recordings also remind the children how they carried out the calculation when they report back to the whole class. Introducing them to useful forms of informal recording helps to build up a repertoire of useful techniques.

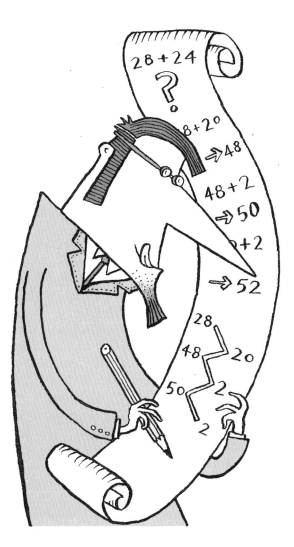

*Standard written methods*
Another role of paper and pencil methods is when following a given structure for doing calculations. The standard algorithm for long multiplication, for example, provides a routine for doing the calculation without having to think it out each time. Once you have firmly committed the routine to memory, you can do calculations with minimum demands on your memory. This was very important back in the days when clerks had to complete ledgers full of calculations and some still consider it a useful skill at the beginning of the 21st century.

*Formal presentation*
Sometimes children need to make a formal presentation of their work for a class display or for a class discussion. This may involve writing about the mathematics, making tables and charts, and finding appropriate visual ways of displaying their ideas. They need to be taught many of these techniques and to analyse each other's presentations for clarity and efficiency.

## Appropriate methods

Children need to be flexible in the approaches that they use; they should not use a particular method just because a calculation is set out in a certain way. Evidence from the national tests and other sources suggests that if children are given a calculation in vertical format, they assume that they are expected to use this method, even when they might do it more quickly and easily – and be less prone to error – if they work it out mentally.

For these reasons, the emphasis in the *Framework for Teaching*

*Mathematics* is on giving children calculations in a horizontal format. Children are then in a position to decide what method of calculation to use. Encourage children to ask themselves: 'Am I confident that I can do this in my head or do I need to make some recording? If I need to make recordings, will jottings do or shall I use a standard method?'

The Framework outlines many of the different methods that children might use. So, in order to do 5003 – 4998, children might count up from 4998 to 5003 in ones, or start with 5003, subtract 3 and then 2, or use some other method.

If children can only read '5003 – 4998' as '5003 take away 4998', then they are likely to set it out as a written subtraction ('take away'). But if they know that it is possible to read the calculation as 'what is the difference between 5003 and 4998?' or 'how many do I have to add to 4998 to make it up to 5003?' then they have opened up the range of calculation strategies.

## Stages of learning about calculation

Pupils should:

Stage 1: Work things out mentally and, if necessary, use jottings.

Stage 2: Work with a repertoire of mental strategies.

Stage 3: Have a secure knowledge of mental strategies, instant recall of number facts and good understanding of place value.

Stage 4: Move from informal jottings to using standard notation.

Stage 5: Refine and make more efficient their mental and written methods.

Stage 6: Be taught compact written methods. ■

# More on intermediate recording

Focusing on mental strategies can cause a gulf between mental and written mathematics. But writing things down can give children much-needed support with mental activities.

## From counting to figuring out

Part of a project funded by the Nuffield Foundation, called Raising Attainment in Numeracy, meant working alongside a group of teachers with mathematically low attaining Year 3 pupils. One common characteristic of these pupils was an over-reliance on counting procedures to find the answers to calculations. While such pupils knew some number facts – most could double single digits for example – they did not use these known facts to figure out results that were not immediately obvious to them. A main aim in the project was to see whether we could help such pupils rely less on counting procedures and make more use of known and derived facts.

Ben was fairly typical in this respect. He knew that 4 + 4 = 8 but could not make the link that 4 + 5 must be 9. Every time Ben was asked to do a calculation he treated it as a new situation to be worked out afresh, so rather than using his knowledge of 4 + 4 to find the answer to 4 + 5 he wanted to use a counting method. The key to helping Ben's

difficulty was to get him to make some intermediate recording. His teacher asked Ben to place 4 counters in each of two pots and record on slips of paper the situation, a known fact which he could do.

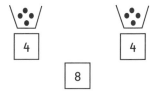

Ben's teacher then asked him to add another counter to one pot and to consider whether the number cards were still correct. Ben not only knew that they were not but was able to correct the recording to match the new situation. Most pleasingly, he could then do that without recalculating the total but by using his recorded known fact.

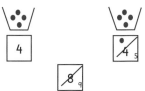

The teacher reported a marked change in Ben's approach to mathematics after making this connection, demonstrating an

*Ben had to make some written recording to keep track of the various pieces of information*

awareness that it was something he could do in his head rather than having to rely on external counting materials.

Thinking about this incident, we realised that we had fallen into the trap of keeping the mental and the written separate. We were so keen to work on Ben's mental strategies that we had assumed that the written had no place. But for Ben to make sense of the situation, some form of written recording was essential in helping him hold on to the various pieces of information.

## Jottings to aid strategies

Just as recording his known fact helped Ben work on a derived fact, so the use of intermediate jottings can help children develop more sophisticated mental strategies. One device that appears to be particularly effective in helping pupils is the use of a blank number line. Rather than using number lines with the unit divisions marked – which may encourage children to continue to count in ones – an empty line allows them to decide on the most appropriate 'jumps' to make. For example, to add 36 and 22 on an empty number line a child may choose to do something like:

*I am starting at 36 and first I am going to add on 20*

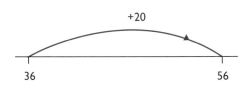

*Then I add on the 2*

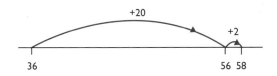

*So, 36 and 22 is 58*

## Models for multiplication

A popular introduction to multiplication is to link it to addition, introducing it through repeated jumps on a number line. The number of jumps is specified and the size of each jump given.

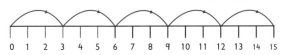

*Five equal jumps of 3*

$5 \times 3 = 15$

While this is an important and useful image, the rectangle is valuable in that it can provide a good bridge between the mental and the written. Objects or squares laid out in rows and columns provide a strong visual image of multiplication that complements the use of repeated addition.

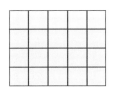

$5 + 5 + 5 + 5 = 20$
*Four rows of five is 20*

One advantage that this image has over jumps on the number line is that the commutativity of multiplication is easier to see – all you have to do is rotate the rectangle through 90º.

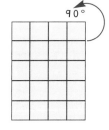

*Intermediate jottings can help children develop more sophisticated strategies*

*4 × 5 is equivalent to 5 × 4*

It is not quite so obvious that four jumps of five on a number line will land you in the same place as five jumps of four.

## Developing long multiplication

Later, children can begin to work with rectangles where the side of each square represents ten in order to multiply multiples of ten together.

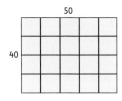

$50 \times 40 = 20 \times 10 \times 10 = 2000$

At the next stage the detail in the diagrams can be reduced.

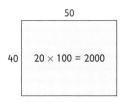

It is now a short step to working with diagrams like this.

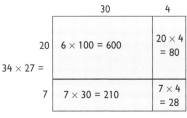

$600 + 210 + 80 + 28 = 918$
so $34 \times 27 = 918$

Soon children can carry out the multiplication without the diagram, but have this image to fall back on if they are unsure about their workings.

$$
\begin{array}{rrrr}
53 \times 46 & 50 \times 40 & = & 2000 \\
 & 50 \times 6 & = & 300 \\
 & 3 \times 40 & = & 120 \\
 & 3 \times 6 & = & 18 \\
\hline
 & & & 2438 \ \blacksquare
\end{array}
$$

# Towards formal recording

Children often fall down in mathematics when they fail to understand *why* a calculation works. So how can we develop the written methods that show the working behind the numbers?

## Traditional methods

Adults who were taught in the '50s and '60s often learned to do paper and pencil subtraction using 'equal addition' – ten to the top and ten to the bottom. And while equal addition is an efficient method, it is not easy to explain why it works – hence the move towards using 'decomposition' as the standard method. But even methods such as decomposition seem obscure to many children, and can prevent them from understanding what they are doing.

## Bugs

Daniel is working through a page of subtractions of tens and units. Here is some of his working:

$$
\begin{array}{r}
56 \\
-24 \\
\hline
32
\end{array}
\qquad
\begin{array}{r}
63 \\
-37 \\
\hline
34
\end{array}
$$

$$
\begin{array}{r}
78 \\
-55 \\
\hline
23
\end{array}
\qquad
\begin{array}{r}
82 \\
-49 \\
\hline
47
\end{array}
$$

It is easy to spot that Daniel's errors arise out of a 'bug' in his method: always subtracting the smaller digit from the larger. The idea of bugs comes from the work of J S Brown and R R Burton. Their research, and that of others, indicates that children's errors in arithmetic arise out of three sources:

– carelessness

– lack of knowledge of number

– 'bugs' in procedures

The evidence suggests that errors in written methods are more likely to arise from 'bugs' in children's thinking than from carelessness or lack of knowledge of number bonds. Daniel is typical of the many children who do not treat numbers in a holistic way, focusing instead on the single digits. This could be due to introducing children to calculations in a vertical form before they actually need to write them in this way. However, many texts set such calculations out vertically to lay the 'foundation' for later calculations.

Maybe all that children like Daniel need is lots more practice. However, there is little evidence that more practice helps – and children need to develop understanding as well as facility if they

are to become effective at computation. One way to help develop this understanding is to use paper and pencil methods in which the working is more 'transparent'. The simplest way to do this is to use some form of extended notation.

## 'Transparent' methods for addition and subtraction

When adding, say, 42 and 36 mentally most adults – and children – will start with the tens. When adding 549 and 386 mentally people start with the hundreds. Children find the strategy of starting with the most significant (that is, the most 'valuable') digit helpful when working mentally, so when introducing them to paper and pencil methods it makes sense to choose one that builds on this strategy. For example, to add 549 and 386 one method would look like:

$$
\begin{array}{r}
549 \\
+386 \\
\hline
800 \\
120 \\
15 \\
\hline
935
\end{array}
$$

A good context for introducing paper and pencil methods of addition is asking children to total strings of numbers. These are difficult to deal with mentally, so pencil and paper is useful, and again the method of starting with the most significant digits is a good one. For 45 + 5243 + 3 + 267 + 3189 the working might look something like:

```
      45
    5243
       3
     267
  + 3189
  ──────
    8000
     500
     220
      27
  ──────
    8747
```

When presenting addition and subtraction problems to children for dealing with 'transparently', bear in mind the importance of how they are presented. If you present calculations to children in a horizontal format they can choose how to set them out – perhaps as a vertical calculation but perhaps not. For example, when totalling 45 + 5243 + 3 + 267 + 3189 a child might decide that it is sensible to rearrange the numbers, by adding the 3 to the 267 and the 45 to the 5243 so the calculation becomes 5288 + 270 + 3189. Had this calculation been presented in a vertical format, this method might not have occurred to the child.

Children can be shown how to do subtraction using adding–on methods (a version of 'shop-keepers addition'):

```
    525        378
  − 378      +  2      2
            ─────
              380
            +  20      22
            ─────
              400
            + 100     122
            ─────
              500
            +  25     147
            ─────
              525
```

Alternatively, the subtraction can be done as a 'take-away' – again, in manageable steps. The method shown below was invented by a child as a result of the teacher challenging the class to have a go at carrying out a subtraction for which they had not been taught a formal method.

```
              525
            − 378
  − 300      225
  −  20      205
  −  50      155
  −   5      150
  −   3      147
  ─────
    378
```

## Transparent methods for multiplication and division

Using an area diagram as a model for multiplication can lead to an extended method without the diagram.

45 × 28 =

|  | 40 | 5 |  |
|---|---|---|---|
| | 40 × 20 = 800 | 5 × 20 = 100 | 20 |
| | 40 × 8 = 320 | 5 × 8 = 40 | 8 |

800 + 320 + 100 + 40 = 1260

leading to

```
  45   ×   28
  40   ×   20   =   800
  40   ×    8   =   320
   5   ×   20   =   100
   5   ×    8   =    40
                   ────
                   1260
```

The traditional paper and pencil algorithm for division is based on repeated subtraction but the density of the layout masks this. Children can be introduced to other paper and pencil methods for division which are still based on repeated subtraction but where the working behind the method is clearer. Such methods depend on confidence in multi-

When was the last time you did a standard paper and pencil long division?

plying by 10, halving (to multiply by 5) and doubling.

For example 186 ÷ 8.

```
    186
  −  80    (8 × 10)
  ─────
    106
  −  80    (8 × 10)
  ─────
     26
  −  24    (8 ×  3)
  ─────
      2
```

Answer: 23 remainder 2

You may well feel that these extended methods are more time consuming to do than the standard ones. Well, yes, they are – a bit. But think of the time saved on drilling children in methods that many find difficult to remember. And when was the last time you did a standard paper and pencil long division – outside the classroom, that is? ∎

# Mathematical problems

Many children underperform with word problems simply because they expect to spot quickly the mathematics involved. Deciding which operation to use can be challenging for children, as the wording of a problem can dramatically alter the level of difficulty.

We often talk about 'problems' in mathematics lessons as though they were a single set of things. However, a problem can take many different forms.

For example:

- How much would the ingredients cost to bake a birthday cake?
- Have I got enough time to bake it before I go out?
- Can you cut a cake into eight pieces with exactly three cuts? (No horizontal cutting allowed.)
- Jenny baked 24 muffins. Three-quarters of the muffins were blueberry. The rest were chocolate. How many muffins were chocolate?

### Problems one and two

The first two problems in the list could both be described as 'realistic' or 'real life' problems – both are situations that you could meet in everyday life and to which you might need a solution. However, only the first of them is likely to appear in a mathematics text book. The second requires measurement and approximation but is more of a practical than a mathematical problem.

### Problem three

The third problem, although set in the context of cakes, is hardly realistic at all. If you really needed to cut a cake into eight pieces, then the number of cuts would not be restricted. However, we should not dismiss such problems. Introduced in an appropriate way, this kind of problem can tap into children's curiosity and provoke some rich mathematical thinking.

### Problem four

But what about Jenny and her muffins? What sort of problem is this? It is not realistic – if Jenny wanted to know how many muffins were chocolate she would count them. And it is not of much mathematical interest, as Problem 3 is. Such problems are really calculation exercises wrapped up in words. The case for putting calculations into a real-world context like this is that it gives meaning to mathematical ideas. However, a warning is necessary: if children have an exclusive diet of artificial problems such as this they may come to think of mathematics as an obscure subject that has little use to them.

## Posing problems

Analysis of children's performance in the national tests suggests that there are at least two difficulties that children encounter in dealing with numerical problems:

- they have difficulty in making the connection between the previously taught mathematics and problem contexts – rather than use the mathematics they have learned to solve the problems, many children fall back on simpler methods to solve them

- children tend not to try to make sense of the problems posed in mathematics lessons in realistic terms – they focus mainly on the mathematics, stop at the point of reaching a mathematical solution and fail to reinterpret this into the real context of the problem

Three aspects need to be thought about when posing problems for the children to solve:

- the effect of the context chosen
- the effect of the complexity of the calculation involved
- the need to interpret the solution

### Effect of the context

In 1994 national tests, Key Stage 1 children were asked:

$56 \times 100 = ?$

*Sam has 50p. Chris has 10 times as much. How much has Chris got?*

Both of these questions assess children's understanding of the effect of multiplying by a power

**Children have difficulty in using the mathematics they know to solve word problems**

of 10. The analysis of test results showed that children had difficulties with place value in both questions, but fewer were able to answer the second question, even though the numbers are simpler in this 'context' question.

Children whose experience of problem solving is limited to contrived situations, created to embody a particular calculation, often learn that the context of the problem is not particularly relevant. They come to treat the context as 'window dressing' and ignore it. Instead, they choose an operation based on the size and type of numbers involved. A child might decide that a problem containing the numbers 3 and 12 must be multiplication, on the basis of knowing that the page of problems is meant to be challenging, and simply adding or subtracting the numbers would be too easy.

Another strategy which children develop to help them deal with word problems is to try to spot 'key' words in the problem that will enable them to 'identify' which operation to use. For example, a child may decide that 'more' is associated with addi-

*There needs to be variety in the range of contexts and in the level of difficulty*

tion (Jim has five marbles and he wins three more. How many does he have now?). But there is no simple one-to-one match between words and operations. Consider the different senses of 'more than' in each of these questions:

Jane has eight marbles more than Jo. Jo has five marbles. How many marbles does Jane have?

Jane has eight marbles. Jo has five marbles. How many marbles more than Jo does Jane have?

This indicates that there is no simple relationship between whether children find questions 'in' or 'out' of context easier; their degree of familiarity with the context will affect their interpretation of it. In both teaching and assessing word problems teachers need to provide a range of contexts, some of which are familiar to children, others that are less familiar, and talk through both the real-life and mathematical interpretations with the children.

### Effect of the complexity of the calculation

The Assessment of Performance Unit presented 11-year-olds with questions involving $4 \times 37$ and $9 \times 37$ in the context of money:

*Tariq's cat is called Sammy. Sammy eats four tins of cat food each week. Each tin costs 37p. How much does Tariq spend on cat food for Sammy each week?*

*Josephine's dog is called Reggie. Reggie eats nine tins of dog food each week. Each tin costs 37p. How much does Josephine spend on food for Reggie each week?*

The success rate on the first question was 52 percent but this dropped to 39 percent on the second question – which is basically the same problem, using slightly 'harder' numbers.

### Interpreting the solution

The context also has an effect in terms of children interpreting their solutions. The following question is typical:

How many adults are needed to accompany a party of 427 children if one adult accompanies each group of 15 children?

Only a small proportion of children gave the correct answer of 29. Many gave an answer of 28. Others gave answers of 28·4666667 by doing the correct operation on a calculator but failing to interpret the answer in the context of the problem. Some did the division using paper and pencil but still failed to interpret the remainder correctly.

### Summing up

All this suggests that the teaching and assessment of 'realistic' number problems needs to provide children with variety. This variety should be in the range of contexts and the level of difficulty within the context.

This method will enable you, when assessing children, to diagnose difficulties. At the same time, you will be able to provide the children with the range of experiences to help them develop problem-solving skills. ∎

# Starting with problems

Used in the right circumstances, word problems not only provide suitable real-life contexts for mathematics but can also help children to develop a thorough understanding of number operations.

## Start with the mathematics or start with the problem?

A popular belief in teaching mathematics is that children need to learn mathematical skills and procedures – how to subtract or multiply for example – before they learn to use these skills in a problem-solving situation. According to this belief, problems should be used as a way of applying previously learned mathematical skills. But contexts can help children make sense of the mathematics and tap into their ability to find a solution that makes sense: problem solving can be used as a means of developing mathematical ideas.

The 'problems as a way of applying skills' approach tends to lead to particular skills being 'wrapped up' in different contexts. For example, number bonds to ten might involve marbles, cakes and counters, all in different situations – the idea being that children come to see that the mathematics can be applied to lots of contexts. In other words, the approach is one-task-in-many-contexts. The 'problems as a way of developing skills' approach has a very different feel to it. One possibility is to take a context and explore all the different ways that mathematics might arise – one situation leading to lots of mathematics, as opposed to one piece of mathematics leading to lots of situations. This is a one-context-many-tasks approach.

### One-context-many-tasks

To illustrate what this one-context-many-tasks approach might look like, take the context of wheels on vehicles going past the school. Having decided in advance how many wheels particular vehicles have, a child could work on problems such as:

– Four cars go past the school, how many wheels were there?

– Three cars, four motorbikes and two six-wheeled lorries go past the school. How many wheels went past?

– Suppose lorries have eight wheels rather than six. What would be the new total?

– I counted the wheels on some cars and lorries. There were 30 wheels and three cars. How many lorries were there?

– Some cars and bikes go past. Together they have 20 wheels. How many cars and bikes might there have been?

These problems can be tackled in various different ways. This open-endedness can lead to rich discussions about efficiency of methods and links between operations. It can also focus children's attention on how they set about choosing which mathematics to use. Once the children get the idea, they can also set problems for each other to explore

## Making decisions

When starting from problems children need to make many decisions, including:

– what information is relevant?

– which operation(s) to use?

– which method of solution to use?

– what would an appropriate answer look like?

### Finding relevant information

Most problems in mathematical text books present the exact amount of information required, no more, no less. In real life, though, solving problems is rarely that simple. Help children to decide what information is relevant by giving them:

*problems where they have to collect information for themselves*

– Can you make an open-topped cube that holds 500 millilitres?

– If you had £100 to spend, what could you buy from this catalogue?

> Providing contexts helps children tap into their ability to find a solution that makes sense

– Have you been alive for a million seconds?

*problems which contain redundant information*

– Amy has £2. Her bus journey costs 75p each way and takes 20 minutes. The bus is due to arrive in 10 minutes. How much change will Amy have after she has made both journeys?

*Which operation?*

Deciding which operation to use is often the most challenging decision, as the wording of a problem can dramatically affect the level of difficulty. Give children practice in deciding what operation to apply by reading out story problems and asking them to write down the keys they would have to press on the calculator to find the answer. Some Year 4 children were asked to do this and were fine with problems involving addition and those that used subtraction in a 'take-away' sense. Other problems gave a more surprising response. For example, the children were asked which calculator keys they would press to find the answer to: 'Jane has 23 sweets and Jo has 15. How many more sweets than Jo has Jane got?' Many children in the class wrote: 15 + 8 =

As they had 'cheated' by working the answer out mentally the teacher then gave them a story that was beyond their mental ability:

Sanjit has 1789 stamps in his album and Rashid has 2456 stamps. How many more stamps does Rashid have?

These same children wrote down that you cannot do this on a calculator!

You can help children work out the operation needed to solve a problem using diagrams. Consider the following:

Joanna had £37 and spent £19. How much did she have left?

$2\frac{1}{2}$ is clearly not a sensible answer to the question, 'How many video tapes at £4 each can I buy for £10?'

Maria has saved £19. She wants to buy a tape recorder costing £37. How much more does she need?

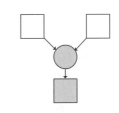

In the boxes, children write the numbers they know, leaving blank what they want to know and adding an appropriate sign in the circle. So for Joanna, they know what she started with and what she spent and can then agree in discussion that the missing operation is subtract.

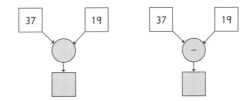

For Maria, what they know is somewhat different – how much she started with and what she wants to end up with, so different boxes are filled in.

*Which method of solution?*

Both the Joanna and Maria problems can be solved using the mathematical model of 37 – 19, but in the second case, children are much more likely to use counting on than 'take away'. This may not matter much when the numbers are small but can cause difficulty if, for example, they count on from 128 to 379. We need to help children appreciate that the mathematical model may not be the same as the realistic situation. One strategy is to work on different ways of expressing the same calculation by having the unknown in different places. For example:

$37 - 19 = \square$ is equivalent to

$37 - \square = 19$

$19 + \square = 37$ and

$\square + 19 = 37$

Children often resist this idea because they have become used to reading the '=' sign as 'makes' rather than 'equals' and the symbol is regarded as the signal to carry out a mathematical action rather than expressing the idea that both sides are equivalent. You can help them overcome this by working on expressing completed calculations in as many equivalent ways as possible.

*What is an appropriate answer?*

Having found a mathematical solution to a problem, children need to decide if their solution is realistic. Ask children to note down the mathematical solution and the realistic solution separately; this can help them see the distinction and will help them to see, for example, that $2\frac{1}{2}$ is not a sensible answer to the question: 'How many video tapes at £4 each can I buy for £10?' ■

# Children inventing problems

Real life can act as a springboard for mathematical calculations, helping children to engage with a problem. But what comes first – the calculation or the context?

## Making sense of the context

The traditional approach to word problems is to take a particular arithmetical skill or number bond and wrap it up in different contexts. This approach can have two unexpected and undesirable outcomes:

– Children think of mathematics as only being applicable to stereotyped situations.

– They do not try to make sense of the situation but assume the operation to be used is signalled through the wording, or the size of the numbers.

It is preferable to encourage children to try to make sense of the whole context of the problem. There is no particular operation they should use, and sharing different possible methods with each other will help them engage with the problem. One way of approaching this is to turn the problem round: by presenting a calculation to children and challenging them to invent real-life situations in which the calculations may arise.

## Sensible questions

Working in groups or with the whole class, choose a simple calculation, such as 25 – 4. Check that the children can find the answer. Invite individuals to invent a story problem that would require the calculation 25 – 4 to find the answer. For example, 'I baked twenty-five biscuits but four got broken. How many were left?' Now provide children with a set of related calculations, such as 36 + 6, 6 + 36, 42 – 6, 42 – 36. Ask them, in pairs, to make up several stories to go with each calculation. The pairs should then swap stories and write which calculation they think goes with each story. While they are working, ask questions such as:

*How did you decide which calculation to use?*

*Is that problem likely to happen in real life?*

*Can you make it more realistic?*

*Is there another way to find the answer to that problem?*

*Can you make up a problem that uses an operation you haven't used up to now – perhaps multiplication or division?*

> There is no simple trick to making sense of a number problem

There is no simple trick to making sense of a story problem. The children must learn to think laterally about the problem. Discuss with them strategies for making sense of the problems and deciding which operation to use – for example, activities such as drawing a picture, modelling the situation with concrete materials, or acting it out, can all be beneficial.

## One step further

Give the children examples of problems and ask them to invent their own, encouraging them to use contexts involving money and common measures of length, mass and capacity. They need to be able to work out the answers for themselves before they offer the problem to others. Here are some examples:

*Money problems*
What is the total cost of a CD at £7·30 and a tape at £3·60? (addition)

Four people won £484 840 between them. How much does each person get? (division)

What is the cost of 125 packets of crisps at 31p each? What change do you get from £50? (multiplication, division and subtraction)

*Measurement problems*
Mina is 1·28 metres tall. Tina is three centimetres taller. How tall is Tina in metres? In centimetres? (addition of decimals)

A bottle of medicine holds 150 millilitres. A teaspoon holds five millilitres. How many teaspoons of medicine in the bottle? (division)

Present children with a calculation and challenge them to invent a 'real–life' situation in which it might arise

Fred got to the library at 3.12 pm. He left at 4 o'clock. How long was he there? (subtraction)

It is worth making sure that you take this context approach for each area of mathematics that you cover in order to check on children's understanding. Include decimals, fractions and percentages, ratio, and negative numbers, to see if the children can put these into sensible context. Here are some examples.

*Percentages, ratio and negative numbers*

35 percent of the children in the class are wearing trainers. What percentage are not wearing trainers? (percentages)

Libby shares out twelve sweets. She gives Sue one sweet for every three sweets she takes. How many sweets does Sue get? (ratio)

A diver is below the surface of the water at –40 metres. She goes up 22 metres, then down 5 metres. Where is she now? (negative numbers)

If children do not produce appropriate suggestions, even though the calculations are well within their scope, this is an indication that they have difficulty in relating that particular abstraction to real life, and offers clues for planning in subsequent lessons.

If children's responses are restricted in some way, this is another indication of where you will need to look for adjustments in their experience and understanding. For example, in subtraction it is common for children to offer many 'take away' situations (I had 42 cards and I lost 36. How many have I got left?), but very few 'comparing' situations (I've got 42 cards and Kim has 36. How many more have I got than Kim?). It may be that children have not experienced enough comparison problems, or that they are not familiar with the language of comparison.■

# Section 2

## Managing the Daily Mathematics Lesson

| | |
|---|---|
| Background to the National Numeracy Strategy | 36 |
| The daily mathematics lesson: the starter | 38 |
| The daily mathematics lesson: main teaching | 40 |
| The daily mathematics lesson: the plenary | 42 |
| Creating the right environment | 44 |
| Working with the whole class | 46 |
| Keeping the class involved: group work | 48 |
| Keeping the class involved: differentiation | 50 |
| Managing mathematical discussion | 52 |
| Working with adult helpers | 54 |
| National Tests | 56 |

# Background to the National Numeracy Strategy

The National Numeracy Strategy offers teachers and children a new framework for mathematical learning. This article assesses the impact of the strategy on classroom practice.

## What you need to teach the strategy

All teachers need a copy of the *Framework for Teaching Mathematics from Reception to Year 6*, and *Mathematical Vocabulary*. The *Framework for Teaching Mathematics* contains key objectives for the yearly teaching programme, planning grids and substantial guidance on how to run the daily mathematics lesson. *Mathematical Vocabulary* identifies the words and phrases that children need to understand and use from Reception to Year 6 if they are to make good progress in mathematics. It is designed to support the *Framework for Teaching Mathematics*.

## Structure of the numeracy lesson

Unlike the Literacy Hour, which prescribes tightly how the lesson will run and how groups are organised, the Numeracy Strategy makes much more flexible suggestions about how to run the daily mathematics lesson. One point – the lesson is not called the numeracy hour in official circles. Instead it is referred to as the daily mathematics lesson. It

*The daily mathematics lesson gives great prominence to mental calculation strategies*

can last from 45 minutes to more than an hour.

But, the lesson has a clear structure. The first 5 or 10 minutes is devoted to oral work and mental calculation, where the whole class works to rehearse, sharpen and develop mental and oral skills. This is followed by the main teaching activity, which lasts for about 30 to 40 minutes and involves teaching the main mathematics ideas of the lesson. The lesson ends with a 10 or 15 minute plenary session, where the teacher works with the whole class to discuss the work done with the children, sorts out misconceptions, and summarises the key learning points of the lesson.

The introduction to the *Framework for Teaching Mathematics* shows how versatile the lesson can be within this structure. The beginnings and ends of lessons are with the whole class – but there is no one particular way of organising this. The main part of the lesson might also be with the whole class or with groups, with pairs of children, or with children working as individuals. Variety is encouraged, and a diversity of teaching strategies suggested.

## Is it compulsory?

The Numeracy Strategy is not a legal requirement – only the National Curriculum and a daily mathematics lesson are statutory. However, it is 'recommended' that schools take it on board, although they are free to decide how much of it to take on. Ofsted will look for the effectiveness of an internal audit and for subsequent plans and their implementation in relation to the Strategy. Schools should either teach a daily numeracy lesson, in line with the Strategy's recommended structure, or put into practice alternative plans. The mathematics co-ordinator and the SENCO should both work with teachers to implement changes in their practice, including setting regular mathematical activities and exercises for the children to do at home.

By 2002, 75% of all 11-year-olds should have reached Level 4

## Aim of the Strategy

The aim of the Strategy is to improve children's numeracy skills by promoting particular styles of teaching which incorporate a greater emphasis on oral work and mental calculation. The daily mathematics lesson has a recommended structure and flow and great prominence is given to the development of mental calculation strategies.

The intention is for 75 percent of all 11-year-olds to reach Level 4 in the mathematics National Curriculum by the year 2002. However, it is recognised that there are different routes to this goal. It is expected that many schools will benefit by implementing all of the recommendations of the Strategy; some by changing just some of their practices – and others by continuing as they are.

## Major changes

The major change that the National Numeracy Strategy brings to schools is the structure of the daily mathematics lesson, and the emphasis on oral work and mental calculation. Where text books have been relied on to provide the content and the pace of a lesson – but the children are not progressing well enough – teachers will need to learn to lead the lesson according to the clear guidance given by the Strategy.

It is a teaching approach trialled by the National Numeracy Project, and reported by Ofsted to be generally successful in raising standards of attainment. Increasing the pace and rigour of lessons, encouraging teachers to run lessons with direct teaching rather than relying on text books, and, most importantly, emphasising mental methods of calculation – these are the foundation of the Government's commitment to improving numeracy standards in our schools. ∎

# The daily mathematics lesson: the starter

It is important that mathematics lessons have a clear structure, with a beginning, a middle, and an ending. So how do we make sure our mathematics lessons begin with a bang?

## The Starter

The starter should be a warm-up session. Use it to:

– inform the class about the main focus of the lesson

– revise mental strategies that the children have already learned

– develop and explain new mental strategies

– practise the instant recall of number facts

– introduce new vocabulary

– lead into the main teaching

*Informing the class about the main focus of the lesson*
You know what the objectives of the lesson are: it's a question of telling the children in a way they will understand, so that they are prepared for what they are meant to be learning. For example, you might say the lesson is about:

– putting numbers in order

– adding and subtracting tens and thousands

– number patterns in the multiplication tables

– making multiplication easier

– decimal numbers and dividing numbers by ten

> The start of the lesson should be a warm-up session

*Revising mental strategies that the children have already learned*
It is useful to build up a collection of short games and activities, for a whole class, that practise specific mental strategies. It is also helpful to have a collection of demonstration resources available for these activities, such as large number cards, a demonstration 1–100 grid, a class number line and large dice. The blackboard, whiteboard, or flip chart are essential here, and an overhead projector could also be useful. Here are some examples of activities:

– Counting on and back round the class, in ones, twos, fives, tens, hundreds, and so on. Count quickly, slowly, in the voice of different animals, whispering, saying nonsense words such as forty-nine twizzlewhits, fifty twizzlewhits, fifty-one twizzlewhits...

– 'Guess my number' games, where the range of numbers and the kinds of questions to be asked can be defined: 'I'm thinking of a number between 0 and 100' (or 50 and 150, or 0 and –100, or a half and three-quarters...). The thinker can only answer 'yes' or 'no' to the questions.

– Putting digits in order. Children can work in groups of three, or as two, three or four teams. Display two, three or four digits on large cards, or write them on the **board or overhead projector;**

Build up a collection of short games and activities for the whole class

children make the largest or smallest number they can with the digits. Extend this by using the digits to make fractions or decimal numbers.

– Buzz: Children count round the class in ones, but the child whose turn it is to say 'three' or any multiple of three says 'buzz' instead. You **can choose any**

multiplication table you wish the children to practise.

A harder version is Fizz-Buzz where, in addition, multiples of five are replaced with 'fizz'. A multiple of both three and five would be 'Fizz-Buzz'.

– Use a demonstration 100-grid to practise addition or subtraction or doubling or halving. As you point to particular numbers, ask the children to add 10 or subtract 1, or double or halve the number.

*Developing and explaining new mental strategies*
For example, start the lesson by counting on and back in tens from any number, and in ones from any number. Then demonstrate on the board how adding 9 is the same as adding 10 and subtracting 1.

*Practising the rapid recall of number facts*
Suggest ways of remembering facts children need to know instantly; for example, the products in the four times table are double those in the two times table; the products in the five times table end in 0 or 5; the digits of the products in the nine times table always add to 9 and so on. You can also give them strategies for remembering number facts, such as rhymes, chants and mnemonics.

*Introducing new vocabulary*
You need to plan what new vocabulary to introduce, how to use it with the children, and how to illustrate or explain it.

*Leading into the main part of the lesson*
The main part of the lesson will follow on from the introduction naturally. The main part can either be a progression of work carried out in the previous lesson, or the presentation of new work, and will be organised in whatever way you have planned. ■

# The daily mathematics lesson: main teaching

During the main part of the lesson you could be working with the whole class, groups, individuals or pairs of children. Within each of these situations we need to cater for a variety of learning styles.

## Main teaching

We now know from research that different people have different preferred learning styles – and that this applies as much to children as adults. While one child may benefit from a practical 'hands-on' approach to mathematics, another may learn just as effectively by watching others. Some children prefer to bounce ideas off others, while others are more happy to sit in a quiet corner and try to work things out on their own. The implication of this for the main teaching part of the numeracy lesson is that variety needs to be built into it: variety not only in types of teaching, but in ways of working, and the sort of activities the children are undertaking.

*Variety in teaching methods*
While we talk a lot now about whole class teaching, this does not have to be the traditional 'chalk and talk' approach where the teacher goes through exercises to be done and then sets children off to work individually on practice exercises. In lessons where you decide that it is appropriate for there to be a high proportion of direct teaching, it

is still possible to vary the style of teaching. Approaches might include:

– demonstrating techniques: for example, using a demonstration protractor to show how to measure angles or using an overhead calculator to demonstrate how to use the memory

– modelling methods: for example, working through a long multiplication of decimals to show how to set it out correctly or talking through the decision making processes in solving a word problem

– managing a discussion: for example, inviting pairs of children to discuss the statement 'all squares have exactly four lines of symmetry' and then discussing as a class whether or not the children think that this is always true, or encouraging the children to discuss which of two different methods demonstrated for doing a subtraction is the more effective and efficient

– supporting children's explanations: for example,

identifying a pair of children to come to the board to explain how they worked out a division and checking that the rest of the class understand the method being shown

– working with misunderstandings: working through a calculation with an error in it and inviting the children to identify what is wrong or asking two children who have arrived at different answers to explain their methods and getting the class to discuss which they think is correct.

*Variety in ways of working*
Varying the types of group and group membership can help meet different children's preferred learning styles.

– group work: while research shows that 'near ability groups' (ability groups with some spread of attainment but not too much) may be the most effective way of grouping children, do not get children locked into always being in the same group. Firstly, children's abilities in mathematics are rarely uniform across all aspects of the subject. So a child who is good at number may be less confident in work in shape and space and vice versa. Secondly, some aspects of the curriculum lend themselves to being better worked on in mixed ability groups. In particular, when working on problems in context, lower

> Some children prefer to bounce ideas off each other – others like to work things out on their own

attaining pupils often bring more common sense to bear on the problem than higher attaining children.

– paired work: working in pairs can help children's understanding. A few minutes discussing an idea with a neighbour before a whole class discussion gives children the opportunity to rehearse their ideas and greatly improves the level of subsequent discussion. Pairs can also set problems for each other to work on and check each other's solutions.

– individual work: we tend to treat individual work as something the children do at the end of the lesson after they have all taken part in the explanation of the ideas or task. But a brief period of individual work at the start of a lesson can also be beneficial: it means that children have a few minutes to try to work something out for themselves and so have more ideas to bring to bear on any subsequent discussion.

*Variety in activities*

We know that there are three main preferred learning styles:

**visual**

learners who like to work with visual images, pictures and diagrams

**auditory**

learners who like to hear things and put ideas into words.

**kinaesthetic**

learners who like to act things out and engage in movement.

One reason why the empty number line may be such a powerful learning tool is that it embodies all three of these learning styles. There is the visual image of the positioning and ordering of numbers on the number line, the auditory aspect of explaining how to get from one place on the line to another and the kinaesthetic element of moving in jumps along the line.

When planning mathematical activities it is important to bear these different learning styles in mind. While not every lesson might contain every style, over time your lessons should provide balance in the styles of working catered for. ∎

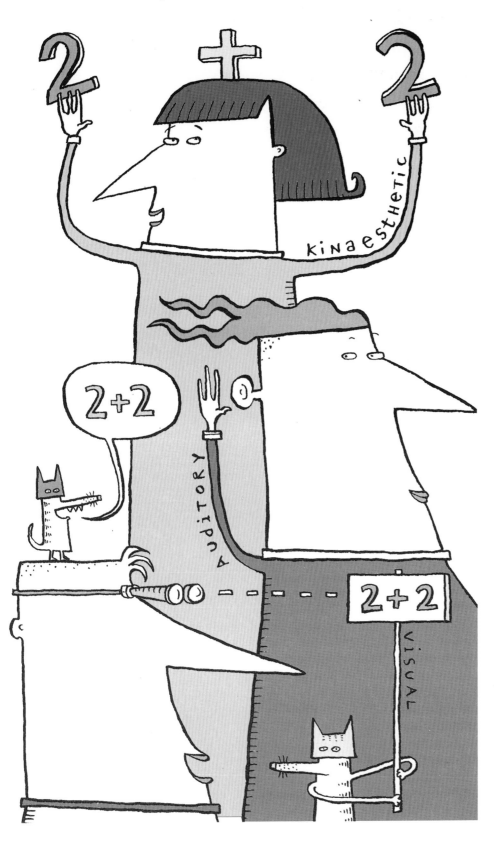

# The daily mathematics lesson: the plenary

A time to reflect on the lesson, summarise key facts and ideas, share discoveries and consolidate progress – the daily mathematics lesson should certainly not be allowed just to fizzle out at the end.

## The plenary

The last 5 to 15 minutes of the lesson should be given over to a plenary, when the whole class come together to:

– present and explain their work to others

– question each other about their work

This session also allows you to:

– assess children's work, give constructive feedback, and evaluate the overall success of the lesson

– plan with children any follow-up work or homework

– remind children what the lesson was about

*Children presenting and explaining their work to others*
Help children to develop their communication skills by presenting work and findings in various ways. It is important for children to articulate their own mathematical processes, as well as listening to and following each other's explanations. They should become used to a range of ways of communicating, such as writing on the board, using an overhead projector, using

> Children need to articulate their mathematical processes

demonstration cards, grids and lines, and presenting work in charts, posters and other displays.

*Children questioning each other about their work*
Children should become used to analysing each other's work. They should have plenty of practice in asking questions of each other in order to further their own understanding. This will take time, interest, motivation and self-discipline, but involvement in this process will engage most children. You will need to provide a model for asking questions during the course of all lessons, in particular for open questions such as:

– Why did you decide to do it this way?

– Why did you organise your results like that?

– Can you talk me through what you have done so far?

– How did you get your answer?

– Can you explain why it works?

– How did you check it?

– What did you learn from it?

*Assessing children's work, giving constructive feedback, and evaluating the overall success of the lesson*

The plenary gives you the opportunity to be honest with children about how the lesson went, and what you think they have achieved.

*Planning with children follow-up work or homework*

A review of the work of the lesson often results in discussion about further work that needs to be done either in a future lesson, or as homework. For homework you can give children a related

Give children plenty of practice in asking each other questions

problem, or some number facts to learn.

*Reminding children what the lesson was about*

End by stating simply the key idea of the lesson, for example:

– If you add or subtract 10 or 100 the units digit stays the same

– Remember, seven 6s are 42

– When adding two numbers, put the larger one first

– There are lots of ways to add and subtract

– You can multiply by doing repeated addition

– You can 'undo' addition by subtracting

Children will very quickly get used to the conventions of a mathematics lesson with a beginning, a middle, and an end, and expect to give their attention to whatever is going on. The key is to plan the whole lesson thoroughly, from the vocabulary you wish to introduce through to the key idea to tell the children at the end; finally, remember to encourage children to discuss and present the mathematics they have done to the rest of the class. ■

# Creating the right environment

Within the structure of the daily mathematics lesson, teachers and children get unprecedented opportunities to learn together – if the environment is conducive to cooperation and participation.

Full participation is one of the main aims of the daily mathematics lesson; in order to maximise the opportunities for children to be fully involved at all times we need to develop classroom environments where both teachers and pupils see themselves as learners, and where everyone works together, taking responsibility for each other's learning as well as their own. Achieving this communal participation relies on four key elements:

– the tasks that children are working on

*Both teachers and pupils need to see themselves as learners*

– the talk that takes place during mathematics lessons
– the tools available to children to help them tackle the mathematics
– the classroom relationships that support learning mathematics.

## Tasks

Those mathematical tasks that develop children's understanding do so by challenging them to solve problems rather than work through routine exercises. One teacher had a bottomless triangular pyramid that, held apex-down, became a container for marbles. Filling this layer by layer, the chil-

Ask, 'How did you work that out?' when a child gets it right – or the child will learn that this question really means, 'You've got it wrong'

dren were challenged to find a way to represent the number of marbles in each layer and of predicting the total number of marbles for a given number of layers. This led to rich discussion about the number patterns and plenty of mental calculation. Tasks like this that do not set ceilings on the level of difficulty enable children to engage with mathematics at different levels of attainment.

## Talk

Talk is integral to the learning environment, particularly when the teacher and the children are able to learn from each other. Children often construct understandings that are not mathematically correct – so encourage them to talk about their methods. Feedback is important for correct as well as incorrect answers – particularly when some explanations may be more powerful than others. One child may explain that to multiply by ten you add a nought while another child says that you are moving the digits up a column. In a way both explanations are correct, but the former ceases to be a useful understanding in the context of decimals. The teacher's role is central in exploring the differences in the explanations.

## Tools

For all types of mathematics we use tools of one sort or another, even if these are simply diagrams and symbols. In mathematics lessons children should use a range of tools to help them carry out the tasks required. They also need to encounter tools that provide models of mathematical ideas. Different children have very different learning styles – some will prefer the visual, some the oral and some the kinaesthetic – and tools for tackling mathematics need to provide a range of experiences to meet these different learning styles. This is why the empty number line is such a powerful mathematical tool: it is visual, children can use it to explain their methods and there is the very satisfying kinaesthetic element of making the jumps along it.

## Relationships

If children are going to be challenged with mathematical problems, if they are going to offer explanations and if they are going to feel free to use the tools that suit them individually, the classroom needs to provide a supportive environment. Children quickly pick up on the way the classroom works. If you never ask them 'How did you work that out?' when their answer is right, they will soon realise that this question really means: 'You've got it wrong'.

When making changes, explain what you are doing and why. If, when one child is explaining his or her method, the rest of the class is more interested in their own methods, ask the children to re-explain the method they have just heard – before asking them to explain their own method. Then talk to the children about why you are doing this. ∎

# Working with the whole class

We know that whole-class teaching is to play a larger part in primary mathematics lessons. But how do we help children to share and present their ideas to the whole class?

The Numeracy Task Force's final report recommended that a high proportion of time should be spent on whole-class teaching. For many people this conjures up images of a teacher at the board talking and, at best, inviting contributions from one or two pupils – usually the keen or bright. But the Task Force insisted that its proposals did not mean a return to the formal 'chalk and talk' approach – and that whole-class teaching should be interactive, lively and stimulating. So what does this really mean in practice? How can we help children to adjust to the change in emphasis and to develop the confidence to share and present their ideas with the whole class?

## Chorus work

The enjoyment of speaking collectively, as one voice, can be put to good use in numeracy lessons. You could, for example:

– explore the patterns made when counting on and back from 0 or another number by chanting as a whole class

– 'bounce' between yourself and the class: you say a number and they say the number that is ten more than or double the amount

– ask the class to read things from the board as a chorus. A place value board is helpful for this – as you tap out a number in the hundreds, followed by one in the tens then the units, the children read it out together.

| 100 | 200 | 300 | 400 | 500 | 600 | 700 | 800 | 900 |
|-----|-----|-----|-----|-----|-----|-----|-----|-----|
| 10  | 20  | 30  | 40  | 50  | 60  | 70  | 80  | 90  |
| 1   | 2   | 3   | 4   | 5   | 6   | 7   | 8   | 9   |

Add fun and variation to whole-class chorus work by asking the children to speak very quietly or in a squeaky or a grumpy voice. Or split the class in two, with each half challenging the other. For example, how long does it take one half to count in threes accurately from 0 to 60? Can the other half better this time?

## 'Show me'

The use of digit cards allows the children to show you their answers individually. Each child needs a set of 0–9 cards. Pose a mental challenge; children show

the answer with their cards but hold these against their chest until asked to turn them to show you. If you also have a set and turn yours around at the same time the children are provided with a check. This approach has a number of advantages:

– it gives everyone time to work out the answer without being distracted by quicker pupils

– only you can see the children's answers, so individuals who are incorrect do not lose face in front of the others

– a quick glance around can help you see the range of answers and get a sense of how well the class as a whole is coping

Questions for 'Show Me' sessions can be simple: 'What do you get if you halve 10?' or harder: 'I'm thinking of a number, I square it, halve the answer and get 18; what was my number?' or very challenging: 'I'm thinking of a number, I multiply it by 6, take one fifth of the answer, double that and get 12. What was my number?'

## Turn-taking

As a variation of chorus work, the children can take it in turns to give answers. The possibilities include:

– pointing with one hand to a number on a 1–100 grid and simultaneously pointing to someone who has to give the number that is 10 more, or

*Avoid early finishers getting bored, or less confident children becoming frustrated*

double... or whatever the focus is

– starting a number pattern, for example, counting back in fours from 100; go round the class, asking each child in turn to say the next number

Such turn-taking is often a little more threatening to individual pupils than chorus work. You can reduce this threat by preceding turn-taking with whole-class chorus work on the same material, in order to rehearse it. Alternatively, select individuals carefully. For example, ask a confident pupil to add 25 to 52; follow this by asking a less confident pupil to add 25 to 53, building on the answer previously given.

## In pairs: 'snowballing'

Pose a problem for the children to work on and ask them to spend just two minutes on their own working on it and making some notes. When the two minutes is up, ask the children to turn to their neighbour and share what they have done so far.

Again, tell them that they have got exactly two minutes for this. After this, pairs can join with others and work in groups of four to agree on a solution. A technique like snowballing has several advantages in helping develop and hold the children's interest:

– the time working alone provides some initial engagement with the problem

– working with a partner provides a 'safe' opportunity for the children to try out their ideas

– working in a group of four provides a range of ideas and strategies to sort through

It is important to keep the time brief to avoid early finishers getting bored or less confident children becoming frustrated.

## Children explaining

Invite individuals or pairs to the front to explain their solutions to problems; this is an effective way of gaining and holding the attention of the rest of the class. It is important that, in order to

maintain that interest, everyone is encouraged to be an 'active listener'. Keep careful control over who is invited to do the explaining. If you simply ask 'who would like to come forward?' certain children will not volunteer and after a few lessons will learn that they need not stand up and talk. If you ask specific children to come forward, you can make sure that over time everyone gets a turn and the children have to be prepared in case they are called upon.

Questions that can help to ensure that the rest of the class are listening include:

*Sian, how does Gupta's method compare with the one you used?*

*Jo, could you show us how to do this calculation using the method that Rhona explained?*

*Connor, could you try to explain Jan's methods in your own words?*

*Does anyone have any questions for Kim?*

*Does anyone have a different method to share with us?* ■

# Keeping the class involved: group work

What are the benefits of working in groups for mathematics lessons? And what is the best way to organise these groups?

Research has been done in America on what happens when small groups of adults work together to solve problems; it was found that group solutions are often of a higher level of thinking and creativity than those of individuals working alone. In school, in addition to this improved quality of learning, working cooperatively offers other benefits: pupils feel better about themselves, learn to relate to each other, become more tolerant and accepting of differences in learning abilities, gain teamwork skills, and generally like school better. However, we have to look more closely at what is meant by 'cooperative working'.

Most of the time when children are said to be working cooperatively, they are doing their work in groups, but there is no group goal or achievement. The children may or may not talk about the task in hand, and ask each other for help, but ultimately the work they do is their own to complete. It is much harder to organise children to work in truly cooperative groups, with a group aim. Cooperative working can have a positive effect on pupils'

learning as long as there is a shared goal for the group, and each pupil is individually accountable for that shared goal. Here are some ways in which this can be done.

## Learning together

Small, mixed-ability groups work collectively on the same task. They are shown how to work together and are expected to do so. This can increase children's understanding of what they are learning, as well as the more general benefits of feeling better about themselves and each other, focusing on the task, and completing work more efficiently. Games, puzzles and investigations, with children working in pairs or threes, are motivating and can encourage children to collaborate with each other on the mathematics in hand. It is expected that there is a shared outcome.

### Examples

One person chooses a number. The next person halves it mentally. Take turns to keep halving. How far can you go? One person in the group can check with a calculator.

> A group should have a shared goal, for which each pupil in the group is accountable

You have ten stamps; they are all 2p or 5p stamps. What are the different possible total values?

## Group problem-solving

The group is given a problem; they discuss how to approach it as well as working together towards a solution. The process and the end result are analysed both by the children and the teacher. This benefits all the children, and increases general collaboration between them. Problems in which children apply the mathematics they know are good for group problem-solving.

### Examples

How much paper does the class use in a day? How many pages will you fill during your school career? How much paper does the whole school use in a year?

Suppose you were given 10p for each school day this month. How much would you get?

## Peer tutoring

A body of work to be learned is shared out among small groups of children. Each group takes responsibility for a different section of the work, and studies it in detail, so becoming an expert on that section. The groups are then shuffled about, and individuals from different groups teach each other what they have learned about their section of the material. This again helps children to feel good about themselves, and positive about learning and school. This is a powerful way of organising children's learning when you want to ensure that

children really get to grips with different mathematical techniques. For example, you could divide the children into three groups, and give each group a different method of multiplication to learn, then each individual will be responsible for teaching someone else that method. Try these multiplication methods:

*Area method*

$$10 \times 4 = 40 \qquad 7 \times 4 = 28 \qquad 17 \times 4$$

*Doubling and halving*

$$17 \times 4 \qquad 17 \times 4$$
$$34 \times 2$$
$$68 \times 1 \quad = \quad 68$$

*Partitioning*

$$17 \times 4 \qquad 10 \times 4 = 40$$
$$7 \times 4 = 28$$
$$68$$

## Team group-learning

Here the teacher asks children to learn some material in preparation for a test. The children are organised in small mixed-ability groups. Rather than teams competing directly with others for higher scores the emphasis is on individual pupil improvement, on how individuals within the group have improved on previous tests. So the incentive is for the group

> The incentive should be for the group to improve the performance of individuals within it

to improve the performance of individuals within it, rather than outdo the performance of other groups. This is an efficient way of encouraging children to learn number facts and times tables.

## Grouping children

Research shows that groups work best when children are of mixed ability – but with a narrow range of attainment in that mixture. It seems that children gain much from having to give detailed explanations to other pupils, and can also gain from asking for such explanations – and these are activities that can happen a lot in mixed-ability groups. However, there are points to beware: children of highest attainment in a group are often asked by other pupils to give explanations; children of lower attainment may ask other children for explanations, and benefit both from the involvement of seeking help, and from the help that they receive. However, if there are children of middle ability in that same group, they tend neither to ask questions nor to give explanations. For this reason, it is best if children are grouped in such a way that there is no distinct 'middle' in a group. It also seems that low attaining pupils achieve

least of all if grouped together as a low-ability group – these pupils respond much better if mixed with some children of slightly higher attainment.

Research on small group work shows that achievement is more equal among boys and girls if mixed sex groups have the same number of each sex in the group. If there are too many boys, the girls tend not to offer explanations, nor to be asked for them; if there are too many girls, they tend to give the boys more than their fair share of attention. An equal balance seems to even things out. Single-sex groups clearly work in a different way, and could be a useful way of organising pupils at times.

If true cooperative group work is to succeed in the classroom, children need to know exactly what is expected of them. Groups should anticipate that they will need to make cogent reports to the teacher and to the whole class – either as verbal feedback or as written accounts of what they have done. They must expect to have to justify their work and to answer questions about it. The reward is greater self-esteem, higher attainment, and a more positive attitude to school and learning. ■

# Keeping the class involved: differentiation

An emphasis on whole-class teaching doesn't mean that differentiation in the mathematics lesson is a thing of the past. But the *way* we differentiate may need to change.

One of the main aims of the National Numeracy Strategy is to work towards a narrower range of attainment in classes. The Strategy acknowledges that differentiation is still necessary but stresses the importance of keeping it controlled and manageable. Here are some ways in which to include children with a range of abilities.

## Targeted questioning

Target questions to particular children during whole-class work. This is an effective way of differentiating to meet individual needs. It may require a change of teaching style; instead of asking questions and inviting children to put up their hands, you need to select questions to match a particular child's ability. This has the added benefit of helping to keep all the children engaged with the lesson.

## Example

In a lesson on mental addition of two-digit numbers, the general level of expectation for the class might be the addition of two numbers where the units total less than ten – for example, 23 + 45, 32 + 16, 54 + 35 and so on.

To gain the children's interest and involvement, try to pitch the first few questions at a level that all children can manage. But as the session progresses, target questions to individuals. You could challenge more confident children to answer questions where totalling the units crosses the tens boundary, for example:

*Meg, can you do 38 add 24?*

*Jasmin, try 57 add 36*

Encourage less confident children to join in by adding whole multiples of 10:

*Kieran, what is 38 add 20?*

*Dee, can you add 50 and 30?*

Allow children time to explain their methods. This benefits everyone: the less confident feel that their ideas are just as valuable as those of the others and also get to hear more sophisticated methods described by others.

## Open-ended questions

Using open-ended questions encourages all children to take part. These can be combined with targeted questions.

*What numbers can you make using each of the digits 4, 5 and 6 and any of the four operations?*

*Differentiate by targeting questions to particular children*

*Esther, can you make 15? Winston, can you make 34?*

*I have four coins in my pocket. How much might I have? Rashid, could I have exactly 20p? How? Kate, could I have exactly £2·20? What would the coins be?*

*The answer is 19. What is the question? Amy, can you give me a question that involves division? Josh, can you give me a question that involves subtraction?*

## Open-ended methods

Provide for different levels of attainment by allowing children to choose their own method of finding the solution to the same challenge. Put such challenges into meaningful or intriguing contexts to engage interest; problems in context are also less likely to suggest a particular method of solution. You can then ask children to share their methods and lead a discussion about the effectiveness of the different methods used.

## Examples

*Parveen counted 30 legs in the field. How many cows and hens could there have been?*

*Lauren is saving up to buy a book costing £6. She saves 60p a week. How many weeks must she save to buy the book?*

*I have stuck 125 stickers in my album. The album holds 500 stickers. How many more do I need before it is half full?*

## Pupil choice

Activities can often be presented in ways that allow

children some choice over the level of difficulty. For example, rather than putting up ten different addition calculations on the board for children to work through, you could put up two circles of numbers.

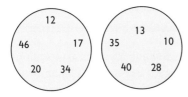

Children select one number from each circle and make up ten calculations of their own choice. Contrary to many people's expectations, rather than choosing easy numbers, children tend to challenge themselves. In addition to meeting individual needs, this type of activity provides useful formative assessment information and reveals children's confidence levels. Marking can be reduced by getting the children to work in small groups to check each other's solutions – noting any calculations that they are uncertain about to bring to a whole-class plenary.

## Different tasks

In the main body of the lesson there may still be times when the class is organised into groups and different activities set for each. In order to keep this manageable, the Numeracy Task Force suggests restricting the number of different levels to three, although the middle group might be split into two groups doing the same activity. This should mean that at least two of the groups can benefit from some focused teaching during this part of the lesson. Once again, everyone should be able to share something of what they have been doing at the end of the lesson, so the three activities need to be organised around a common theme.

### Example

In a lesson on multiplication facts, three different activities could be set up all based around a 10 × 10 multiplication table with every other number blanked out. The lower attainers could work on filling in the blanks on the square. The middle group could work in pairs, cutting up the table into twenty-five 2 × 2 squares, mixing these up and then reassembling the table. The higher attainers could similarly cut up the table into twenty-five 2 × 2 squares and, selecting a single piece at random, figure out the missing numbers.

## Amount of explanation

Some children need more explanation than others before they understand exactly what is required of them in an activity. When explaining a lesson's work, some children could be sent off to start while others remain with you for further explanation. One teacher I know frequently stops during her setting up of an activity to ask:

*"Right, who thinks they understand what I want them to do? OK, off you go and start. The rest of you stay here."*

She then repeats until everyone is happy that they understand. ∎

*"Right, who understands what I want them to do? OK, off you go..."*

# Managing mathematical discussion

Many of us have been conditioned into thinking that mathematics is about children burying their heads in an activity book for half an hour. It's time to change the way we work – and begin to *talk* about maths!

When we were at school, mathematics lessons were conducted in silence. We worked silently, and struggled individually to make sense of the teacher's explanations. History lessons were not like this – we debated the pros and cons of the French revolution. In RE we argued about the existence of God. But we learned that mathematics was a silent discipline where you strove on your own to attain right answers. Teaching has changed a lot since then but attitudes to mathematics are still peculiar. We read children stories and expect a full discussion about what might happen next. We conjecture about what might float and sink and give reasons. But, in mathematics, too often we just give children pages 6 and 7 to do with no debate.

## Developing understanding

We should have more confidence in our own gut feeling about how children make sense of things. Structured talk and discussion helps children develop their understanding of the ideas they are articulating, encourages them to listen to the opinions of others and to argue their corner and modify their vision. We know this. But do we really believe that the same applies to mathematics?

Mathematics has its own internal logical structure that, when you know how it operates, feels obvious and easy. This is why good mathematicians often make lousy teachers – they cannot envisage how anyone could not understand what is so glaringly clear to them. Imagine a mathematics lesson where you are being taught that all angles in a triangle add up to 180°. You understand the words and the logic, but you don't really believe it. It may work for this particular triangle – but does it work for every triangle? This is when you need to debate it, to clarify why you feel deep down that it can't be so. Gradually, through discussion, trial and error, demonstration, experience and, above all, continued expression of your understanding, you may well get to believe that all angles, in every triangle, truly add up to 180°.

Children have the same problems with mathematical ideas. To

> In RE we argued about the existence of God, but mathematics was a silent discipline

overcome these misconceptions they need to debate amongst themselves, with challenges from each other and from you. Try taking the role of devil's advocate. Set up a problem and ask for solutions. If the children provide different answers, ask them whether this matters and, if so, how they might resolve the problem. In debating among themselves the children will reach a definition, which you can clarify and reiterate after the discussion.

## Mathematical vocabulary

In order to discuss ideas, we need to know the words to express them. Mathematics is a precise discipline. The words used have definite meanings. We need to teach these words to children, and help them understand the meanings. The National Numeracy Strategy's *Mathematical Vocabulary* lists all the mathematical vocabulary that primary children need to learn. In Year 1 there is 'difference between' and 'how many more to make...'; in Year 3 'below zero' and 'approximately', and in Year 6 'integer' and 'counter example'. The vocabulary invokes sets of mathematical ideas that need careful teaching.

In learning new terminology, children go through stages of learning. They first need to hear adults using the words in contexts that make them clear, and in practical situations. Then they can hear and use the words in more abstract situations through discussion. Only then are they able to go on to reading and

Mathematics lessons can be stimulating, contentious and intellectually invigorating

writing the words in a meaningful way.

It's often too easy to wade in and provide answers. Instead, ask children a question and then wait for three seconds before speaking. The most useful questions to help children's mathematical development are those that extend their thinking. Sometimes you will want to ask closed questions but generally open questions are best for challenging children's ideas and encouraging them to use and apply their mathematical knowledge and understanding. *Mathematical Vocabulary* gives useful examples of how closed questions can be modified into open questions.

*Closed questions*
*Does that symbol mean add or subtract?*

*Does that fact help you?*

*Can you count the buttons?*

*What do 4, 2 and 7 add up to?*

*Is 24 an even number?*

*What is 6 × 5?*

*What are four threes?*

*Is 16 an even number?*

*Open questions/challenges*
*What does that symbol mean?*

*How does that fact help you?*

*How could you count the buttons?*

*What even numbers are greater than 10?*

*If 6 × 5 is 30, what else can you work out from the fact?*

*Tell me two numbers with a difference of 2*

*What numbers can you make using these symbols: 2, 3, 6, +, −, =?*

*Tell me an even number between 10 and 20*

Questions are also important for focusing children's mathematical

thinking processes and for encouraging reflection. You need to build up an armoury of questions appropriate for different occasions:

*Why do you think that?*

*Is there another way of doing it?*

*What if you tried another number?*

Lesson plans involve planning the mathematical talk as well as the content. You need to be clear about how you will introduce the lesson, what discussion will take place and how you will manage it. You should have in mind the questions you will ask the children, both as they discuss and as they work. You also need a list of the vocabulary you intend to use. In this way mathematics could be the most stimulating, contentious and intellectually invigorating lessons that the children experience in their school lives! ■

# Working with adult helpers

Adult helpers bring a wide range of skills and knowledge to your mathematics lesson – so make sure you take advantage of their presence.

Adult helpers are a valuable resource. But you need to plan carefully how to use them – particularly if they are to help with children's mathematical learning. Be clear about what you can reasonably expect assistants to do, and make sure that you understand what help and guidance they need. Schools should have job descriptions for all types of adult helpers – and teachers should be clear about both the assistant's role and their own management responsibility.

## Types of adult support

*Language support (LAP/bilingual support)*
Trained to support children with E2L and will have valuable skills in developing oral work.

*Special needs support (teachers with a specialist focus, SNAs)*
Employed to work with children on the SEN register; some have specific qualifications, such as working with the hearing impaired.

*Teaching assistants*
Employed for a wide range of tasks; usually untrained but may have valuable personal knowledge about the children in the school.

*Parents and other volunteers*
Willing and enthusiastic volunteers – may have professional qualifications or simply wish to help in their child's school.

## The assistant's support

It is important that your teaching assistant shares your objectives for the children's learning, so that you are both working to the same ends. Try to find time early on in the term to discuss curriculum planning. Assistants need to know what you intend the children to learn and what they should look for in the children's speech and actions to indicate their knowledge and understanding. They must also understand how this fits into the overall progress and development of the children throughout the school.

*Whole-class sessions, both starters and main activities*
Teaching assistants can be fully involved in whole-class sessions. Ask the assistant to sit close to any children who need support, giving them quiet and discreet help:

- counting with them
- encouraging the use of correct language
- reminding the children of previously learned mental strategies such as putting the larger number first, or using known doubles

*Group work*
During main sessions, when the class is divided into groups, adults can help by:

- sitting next to the children, talking through with them what they need to do, and how they might do it
- helping children explain and justify their reasoning, to you and each other
- asking appropriate questions – for example, 'The 4 × 4 square is difficult, but what if it were a 3 × 3 square?'
- reminding children of what they know that might be useful
- helping children use what they know to find out things they don't know

*Plenary sessions*
During the plenary sessions, the assistant can help one group to give feedback to the whole class – perhaps displaying particular skills these children might have, such as specific types of finger counting.

Another valuable use of an assistant's time is as an observer: ask them to focus on particular children and to monitor their responses to the discussion. Agree beforehand what the assistant

> Assistants need to know what you intend the children to learn

should look out for – for example, whether the children appear to follow the lesson, whether they make any attempt to respond to questions and to note any specific responses they make.

## Supervisory help

It can be useful sometimes to ask the assistant to supervise one group of children, while you take another, leaving the rest of the class to work unassisted. You will need to ensure the assistant is clear what is expected of them, and of the children. An assistant can also be asked to move around the class in a supervisory role while you work with a small group. Sometimes the assistant might need to be left in charge of the whole class for a time: provide them with ideas for larger group activities that can be used in these circumstances.

## Appropriate questioning

Whatever the role of the assistant in your classroom, they are an important resource for the children as well as for you. Help them develop their role by learning how to distinguish between closed and open questions, and to look at ways of turning closed questions into open questions. It is not the case that closed questions are 'bad' and open ones 'good' – that is too simplistic – but it is true that adults often use closed rather than open ones. Yet open questions can be invaluable in encouraging children to think for themselves.

## Feedback sheets

Finding time to discuss the day-to-day work in the classroom can be difficult. It is useful to develop a feedback sheet that can be used by you and the teaching assistant, detailing the activity you have planned with the assistant, and the learning objectives and intended outcomes. The assistant

can then record what happens during the activity, and what the children appear to learn. A sample is shown below.

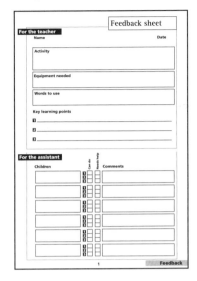

*How to use the feedback sheet*
Before the lesson, fill in the top part of the form. During the lesson, the assistant should:

- discuss with the children what they are doing

- ask open questions to prompt the children's thinking and encourage them to demonstrate what they know and understand

- ask closed questions to find out what facts the children know

- tick the appropriate box and add comments if necessary

After the lesson, the teacher and the assistant should discuss what the children have learned.

## Classroom helpers – some dos and don'ts

Do:
- Plan together if possible

- Have an outline lesson plan, clearly indicating adult deployment

- Ask helpers what they like doing and what their area of expertise is

- Find out if they feel unsure about particular areas of mathematics

- Talk to the INSET coordinator about the school's training plans for adult helpers

- Have vocabulary lists and displays available; if appropriate, provide the definitions as well

- Introduce colleagues properly and make sure they know the school's convention for addressing adults (Are first names acceptable? Does the school always use 'Mr' and 'Mrs'?)

- Provide a box for helpers containing useful information

- Encourage them to use their own ideas and – if it is appropriate – encourage them to use their own experience, for example, managing household budgets or business experience

- Check timetables and notify helpers of changes in arrangements or absent children as soon as possible

Don't:
- Assume that helpers have little mathematics expertise and would prefer to be working with the Literacy Hour

- Assume that adults are familiar with technical vocabulary and the numeracy framework's method of working, for example 'partitioning', 'bridging through 10', 'starting with the significant digit'

- Add children to the helper's group at short notice. ■

*Ensure that the assistants are clear what is expected of them – and of the children*

# National Tests

Children need to prepare for the National Tests – and to have some understanding of what is expected – if they are to demonstrate what they know in the best possible light. Below are some strategies to help them.

## Preparing or cramming?

We are old enough to have taken an 11-plus examination, and can remember being prepared for this by working through booklets of similar types of questions. Many teachers are wary of 'cramming' for National Tests in this way, as the result may be less a reflection of children's understanding and more an indication of their ability to 'question spot'. However, this does not mean that children do not need to be prepared for the test. Having some understanding of what is expected may mean that they can display what they know in the best possible light. This article suggests activities and strategies that, while based around issues arising out of the National Tests, also provide mathematical experiences that are valuable in their own right.

QCA produce a yearly report on children's performance in the National Tests for mathematics. The report contains insights into areas of strengths and weakness, and commentary on individual questions and the mathematical content. But how do we deal with the issues that arise?

## Standard and informal methods

QCA notes that while children cope reasonably well with the layout of questions, it is still important to encourage them to select from a range of strategies and deal with questions presented in a variety of ways.

A glance through test questions reveals a range of presentations. For example, empty boxes are frequently provided to record numbers in. Children need to read the questions carefully to decide what to record in the boxes, as this can vary across:

- writing different numbers in a series of boxes

- writing the same number in a series of boxes

- writing one digit in each box

- writing multi-digit numbers in each box

- writing operation symbols in each box

...and all of these may be presented in either a vertical or horizontal format.

Ensuring that children have worked with a range of presentations helps them give the answer

The result of 'cramming' can be less a reflection of children's understanding and more an indication of their ability to 'question spot'

in the correct format. Another is to give them completed answers showing different solutions – correct and incorrect – and ask the children to discuss whether or not the answers are right.

For example, working in pairs, children can discuss which answers are acceptable solutions to questions such as:

1. Write in numbers to make the answer 36:

   $36 - \square\square + \square\square = 36$

   Child A: $36 - 12 + 12 = 36$

   Child B: $36 - 00 + 00 = 36$

2. This calculation has the same number missing from each box. Write the missing number in each box:

   $\square \times \square - \square = 30$

   Child A: $4 \times 8 - 2 = 30$

   Child B: $6 \times 6 - 6 = 30$

In the first case it is reassuring to realise that a range of solutions are possible, and that you don't have to be 'clever' with your answer. In the second case children need to be clear that while the first answer is mathematically correct it is not appropriate for this question given the constraint in the rubric.

## Realistic contexts

Often, children can correctly carry out a calculation given in symbols, but have difficulty carrying out a similar one set in a real-world context. One reason for this is that children need to coordinate several items of information to make sense of a word

problem. A key item of information may not be immediately obvious and the problem may need to be 'read' in a non-linear way, rather than taking each information item in turn.

Encourage children to 'break set' with the expectation that you start at the top of the page and work down. Challenge this expectation literally by breaking a problem up into several parts and getting children to work cooperatively on solving it.

To turn a problem into a cooperative one, break it down into at least four statements. Write each piece of information on a separate 'clue' card, together with the question to be answered. If the original question does not have four pieces of information, add one or two 'red herring' statements. This helps children learn that not all information may be relevant.

Groups of four are best for working together on cooperative problems. If there are more than four clue cards it doesn't matter if someone in the group has more than one clue. Share the cards out between the group members and ask them to work cooperatively to solve the problem, with two ground rules:

– You can tell the other members of your group what is on your card, but you cannot show your card to the group

– You can only ask for help from the teacher if as a group you cannot sort out why you are stuck

*Help children learn that in problem solving, not all information may be relevant*

Encourage cooperation by providing each group with only one thick pen and a large piece of paper to record their working out on collectively.

One teacher adapted a question from a previous National Test paper to turn it into a cooperative problem as follows:

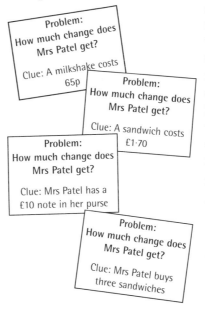

Problem: How much change does Mrs Patel get?

Clue: A milkshake costs 65p

Problem: How much change does Mrs Patel get?

Clue: A sandwich costs £1·70

Problem: How much change does Mrs Patel get?

Clue: Mrs Patel has a £10 note in her purse

Problem: How much change does Mrs Patel get?

Clue: Mrs Patel buys three sandwiches

## Use of language

An issue that QCA has consistently identified as problematic is the appropriate use of mathematical vocabulary. Children display difficulties over:

– words that have everyday meanings as well as specific mathematical ones, for example, 'odd', 'volume', 'product', 'mean', 'difference'

– words that sound similar to other words such as 'sum' and 'some', or 'side' and 'size'

– mathematically specific words like 'equals' or 'equilateral'

'Always, sometimes, never' is a useful activity to help clear up confusion over language and prepare children for questions that require them to explain their thinking. It is also a powerful assessment activity.

Provide children with four or five statements. Working on their own, the children decide whether they think the statement is 'always', 'sometimes' or 'never' true. Then in groups of three or four they have to agree on which category each statement falls into. The whole class discusses the statements and finally children can write their own explanations.

Statements might include:

– finding the product of two numbers is the same as multiplying the numbers

– an equilateral triangle can have a right angle

– adding two odd numbers can have an odd answer

– the greater the perimeter of a rectangle, the greater the area

## Physical conditions

Finally, don't forget that finding the desks laid out differently or having to work without talking for forty minutes, if unfamiliar, can add to children's stress levels and detract from their mathematical performance. There is research evidence that physical activity before intellectual activity can enhance performance, so a brisk walk around the playground before the test might help. ■

# Sample lesson outlines

This section offers three sample lesson outlines for each year from Year 3 to Year 6. The lessons were written by Mike Askew and Sheila Ebbutt to accompany their articles for Junior Education. They have been selected to represent the spectrum of mathematical topics and to illustrate a variety of approaches and ideas.

## Real-life problems

**Year 3**

Making up story problems in which certain calculations are necessary can help children to see their real purpose – and their value – in everyday life.

### Starter

Write on the board:

**2, 4, 5 +, ×, =**

Working in pairs, ask the children to invent calculations with answers greater than 30. They can use any or all of the numbers, and one or both of the operation signs. For example:

$2 \times 5 = 10, 4 \times 10 = 40$    $45 \times 2 = 90$

$25 \times 4 = 100$    $45 + 2 = 47$

### Main activity

Write a calculation on the board, such as:

**53 + 36 =**   Ask the children to make up a story problem for this calculation. Give a range of different examples:

– I have 53p in my money box, and I put in another 36p. How much is in the box altogether?

– I've stuck 53 stickers in my book, and I've got 36 stickers left to stick in. How many stickers will there be in my book when I've stuck them all in?

Make it clear to the children that you are interested in their story, not in the answer to the calculation. Ask the children for their ideas, then put up a calculation that involves subtraction. Can they make up four different stories for the calculation?

**Key idea:** Making up a story about a calculation makes you think about what the calculation means.

### Plenary

Invite the children to present their calculation stories to the class. Encourage others to ask questions if they do not understand the context. Discuss the different ways of representing the same calculation. For example, make sure that the children realise that subtraction can represent 'difference' as well as 'take away'.

### Homework

Ask the children to create some calculations relating to real situations in their own life. For example:

- I have read 52 pages of a 122-page reading book. How many pages do I have left to read?
- I am saving up my pocket money for a CD which costs £15. I receive £2·50 a week and have already saved £10. In how many weeks will I be able to buy the CD?

**Vocabulary**

add
subtract
plus
difference
altogether
total
sum
leave
take away
minus
explain
describe
question
method

## Addition and subtraction

**Year 3**

One of the skills that children need to develop is how to use known facts in calculations. Realising that you don't have to start from scratch each time will be a welcome revelation.

### Starter

Ask the children to write down five numbers less than 10 and to add 6 to each of their numbers. They should then subtract 5 from the answer. When they have done all five, ask them if they notice a pattern, and whether they can think of one quick way to do the two calculations.

### Main activity

Draw two circles on the board and write in the numbers shown below:

15
21    13
44  52  11
42   35

14
32    44
41  33  15
22   25

Ask the children to take one number from each circle and add them together. They should do ten of these, carrying out the calculation in their heads as far as possible.

**Key idea:** When you add tens numbers, you can use your knowledge of numbers that make ten. 50 + 20 is a similar calculation to 5 + 2.

### Plenary

Discuss the different words we use in talking about addition and subtraction and challenge the children to use them in sentences that show their meaning. For example, 'The difference between the number of children in the register yesterday and today is 3, because three children are away today'.

### Homework

Choose a number between 20 and 100. Think of as many addition and subtraction calculations as you can to make that number. Sort out your calculations into different types.

**Vocabulary**

add
subtract
plus
difference
altogether
total
sum
leave
take away
minus

## Numbers and the number system

**Year 3**

Children may have encountered number grids at Key Stage 1, but they are an effective and easily-differentiated tool that can be used in number work at Year 3 and beyond.

### Starter

Put this grid of numbers on the board:

| 1 | 3 | 6 |
|---|---|---|
| 5 | 7 | 10 |
| 7 | 9 | 12 |

Ask the children to find sets of three numbers that total to 20 exactly. How many can they find?

There are six different solutions to this:

**1, 7, 12**       **1, 10, 9**       **3, 5, 12**

**3, 10, 7**       **6, 5, 9**       **6, 7, 7**

### Main activity

Provide the children with grids of squares of different sizes: 1 × 1, 2 × 2, 3 × 3 up to 10 × 10. Ask them on each grid to shade in, for example, the multiples of 3.

| 1 | 2 | 3 |
|---|---|---|
| 4 | 5 | 6 |
| 7 | 8 | 9 |

| 1 | 2 |
|---|---|
| 3 | 4 |

| 3 |
|---|

**Key idea:** Look for patterns by shading in multiples on a number grid.

### Plenary

Ask the children:

What patterns did you find?

Did the same pattern occur in two different grids?

Why might that be?

### Homework

Ask the children to choose ten numbers. They should double each number and add that to the original number.
For example, 6 → 12 + 6 = 18. What do they notice?
Can they explain the pattern?

**Vocabulary**

times

multiply

multiply by

multiple of

product

array

row

column

---

## Multiplication and division

**Year 4**

Don't know your eight times table? Multiply by four and then double the answer! As with many areas of mental maths, doubling is a very useful strategy for multiplication.

### Starter

Challenge the children with some multiplication and division calculations. Each child needs a set of 0–9 cards and you need a set for yourself. Mix up your cards, look at the top one and, without showing it to the children, make up challenges:

– I've multiplied the number on my card by 4 and got 24. What's my number?

– I've divided 30 by the number on my card and got 6. What's my number?

Children should pick out the answer from their set of cards and hold it in the air.

### Main activity

Play 'What's My Rule?' to develop children's knowledge of multiplication. Ask the class for a single digit and record it on the board. Multiply the number by 8 in two steps – multiply it by 4 and then double the answer without explaining your rules to the children:

After a few examples ask if anyone can do the same,

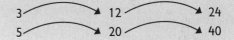

without giving away the answer. When several children have spotted the pattern, discuss the rules you were using. How can they get straight from 3 to 24? What would they multiply by?

Ask the children to work in groups to check that multiplying by 4 and then by 2 does indeed give the same result as multiplying by 8.

On another occasion, work on multiplying by 20 by doubling and multiplying by 10, or multiplying by 5 by multiplying by 10 and halving.

**Key idea:** Splitting a multiplication up into two steps can sometimes make it easier.

### Plenary

Go over the method again and investigate with the children what happens if you reverse the order of calculating – doubling first and then multiplying by 4. Which is easier?

### Homework

Ask the children to write the numbers 1–9 in any order in a 3 × 3 grid and to multiply each pair of numbers that are next to each other – either vertically or horizontally. There are 12 such pairs in total.

**Vocabulary**

double

multiply by

multiply together

# Sample lesson outlines

## Using and applying mathematics

Mental maths is the phrase of the day, but we should not expect – or encourage – children to try to hold too much information in their heads. Paper and pencil jottings are sometimes vital.

### Starter

Begin by giving the children some money problems to work out mentally. For example:

- I bought three pairs of socks at £3·99 per pair. How much did they cost altogether?

- I bought a T-shirt for £7·99 and some shorts for £4·50. How much change did I get from £20?

### Main activity

Ask the children to work in pairs or small groups and to jot down what, and how much, they typically eat in a day. Discuss with the class the amounts of food they eat and ask for ideas about how they could estimate the cost of feeding themselves for a day.

Then, working in pairs or small groups, ask them to estimate how much it would cost to feed themselves for a week, a month or a year.

**Key idea:** When a problem involves several different aspects, record these clearly to keep track of them all.

### Plenary

Ask the pairs or groups to report back on what they did. Discuss the different estimation strategies that they used. Which did they think was most effective?

**Vocabulary**
estimate
approximate
round up
round down

### Homework

Ask the children to select a number of items that would be stored in the refrigerator at home and to estimate the cost of buying them all.

---

## Numbers and the number system

The daily mathematics lesson is intended to be lively and energetic and the use of a wide range of tools in whole-class teaching – such as number grids and cards – can help you to achieve this.

### Starter

You will need a set of nine cards showing the multiples of 5 from 5 to 45. Each child will need a set of 1–9 digit cards.

Ask the children to lay out their nine cards in front of them in a 3 × 3 array. Mix your multiples cards and then turn over and read the top card. The children turn face down the card that shows what 5 needs to be multiplied by to arrive at your total. For example, you read out 30 and they turn over 6. Continue until all the cards have been turned over.

Note: This activity is described as you would set it up for multiplying by 5, but it is easily adapted to other numbers.

### Main activity

| 2 | 3 |
|---|---|
| 4 | 5 |

Ask the children to choose four digits and put one in each square of a 2 × 2 array. They should multiply together numbers that are adjacent to each other, then add together the four products.

In this example, the total is 49. What happens if the numbers are arranged differently?

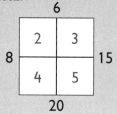

**Key idea:** When you are working on calculations involving multiplication and addition, do the multiplications first.

**Vocabulary**
times
multiply
multiplied by
multiple of
product
array
row
column
add
sum
total
plus
altogether

### Plenary

Ask the children:

- Which arrangement gives the greatest overall total?

- Which arrangement gives the least total?

- How could we adapt this activity to a 3 × 3 grid?

### Homework

The children can use the four digits 1, 2, 3, 4. They can add, subtract, multiply or divide. Using one each of the digits, and treating them as single digits, how many numbers from 1 to 20 can they make? For example:

$1 = (2 + 3) \div (1 + 4)$

$2 = (2 \times 3) - (4 \div 1)$.

## Real-life problems

**Year 5**

Estimating answers can sometimes be very difficult, especially when dealing with large numbers. Scaling down the problem can help you to make a much more accurate guess.

### Starter

Write on the board:

**20, 15, 300, ×, ÷, =**

Working in pairs, ask the children to make as many calculations as they can from the numbers and symbols provided. Put the results on the board. Give other trios of numbers for the children to work on, such as 16, 20, 320, and 11, 18, 198.

$$16 \quad 20 \quad 320 \quad 11 \quad 18 \quad 198$$

### Main activity

Set the children a problem such as:

'How many people could stand in the classroom? In the school hall? In the playground?'

Discuss with the children how they might solve the problem and ask for ideas about how to start. Invite them to make estimates of the space taken by a small sample of children. How close together should the children stand? Following the whole-class discussion, the children can work in pairs or groups to tackle the problem.

**Key idea:** With some problems you can't estimate the answer first, so you have to check your calculations carefully to make sure that they are sensible.

### Plenary

Compare the range of results from the children. Look at the largest estimate and the smallest. Invite one or two pairs of children to explain their calculations, and to justify their results. Discuss with the children ways of checking results by doing the same calculation a different way, and by doing the inverse operation.

### Homework

Ask the children to investigate how much water they drink in a day, in a week, in a year.

**Vocabulary**

approximate

estimate

round up or down

method

strategy

inverse

sign

operation

symbol

equation

reasoning

justify

---

## Fractions, proportion and ratio

**Year 5**

A clear understanding of proportion and ratio can help to reinforce children's understanding of fraction equivalences and strip patterns will help you to clarify this even further.

### Starter

'Mary has two T-shirts for every blouse'.

Work on the different statements and questions that can be made from this information, such as:

- Mary has twice as many T-shirts as blouses.

- She has half as many blouses as T-shirts.

- If Mary has eight T-shirts, how many blouses does she have?

- If Mary has six blouses, how many T-shirts does she have?

### Main activity

Draw some strip patterns on the board and discuss them using the language of 'in every':

In this pattern, one in every three squares is shaded.

- What fraction (proportion) of the squares is shaded? ($\frac{1}{3}$)

- Suppose the strip was 30 squares long. How many squares would be shaded? (10)

- What fraction (proportion) of the 30 squares would be shaded? ($\frac{1}{3}$)

- What about 300 squares long? 3000 squares long?

Key idea: $\frac{3}{9}$, $\frac{4}{12}$, $\frac{10}{30}$, $\frac{100}{300}$, $\frac{1000}{3000}$, are all equivalent to $\frac{1}{3}$.

On another occasion, discuss pattern strips using the language of 'for every':

- In this pattern, there are two white squares for every shaded one.

- What is the ratio of shaded squares to white squares? (1 to 2 or 1:2)

**Key idea:** There are some situations in which you need to know 'how many *in* every...' and some situations in which you need to know 'how many *for* every...'.

### Plenary

Ask the children to make up their own 'in every' and 'for every' statements: 'Two eyes for every child'. 'Five toes for every foot'. 'Two in every seven days are the weekend'.

### Homework

Give the children squared or triangular paper. Ask them to design five different 'one in every...' tiling patterns.

**Vocabulary**

proportion

in every

for every

# Sample lesson outlines

## Addition and subtraction

**Year 5**

The range of number facts that we can store in our heads is quite limited but we don't need to remember everything – we can use what we do know to make quick and accurate calculations.

### Starter

Invite one child to come to the front of the class with a calculator. Ask the class a range of addition and subtraction questions such as:

– What is 89 plus 460?

– What is 580 minus 91?

The child with the calculator has to try to do the calculation quicker than the children doing it in their heads. After several attempts, talk over the quickest way to do these calculations.

### Main activity

**Vocabulary**

plus

minus

tens boundary

hundreds boundary

inverse

round up or down

round to the nearest

Ask the children to choose a three-digit number, write it down, reverse the digits and write that number down, then add the two numbers together. For example: 613 + 316 = 929.

The number they get is a palindrome – it is the same forwards as it is backwards. If it does not make a palindrome the first time, repeat the process. For example: 703 + 307 = 1010 → 1010 + 0101 = 1111.

Working in pairs, the children should record their results and sort them into numbers that make a palindrome on the first addition, on the second addition, on the third addition, and so on. At the end of the session, invite pairs of children to describe their results.

**Key idea:** When you work on a problem, it helps to know your number facts, or to figure them out very quickly.

### Plenary

Give the children a palindrome such as 747. Can they work out the number and its reverse that add up to 747?

### Homework

Using consecutive numbers, try to make all of the numbers from 3 to 50. You can use as many consecutive numbers as you wish in a string.

## Real-life problems

**Year 6**

A good way of sorting through all the information in a problem is to write each statement out on a separate piece of paper – especially when your problem is full of red herrings!

### Starter

Ask the children time problems such as:

– The pop concert started at 19.30 and ended at 02.45. How long did it last?

– The sun sets at 20.30 and rises at 05.30. How many hours of darkness are there?

### Main activity

Write this problem on the board:

> – Ming is going to visit her grandmother in Hong Kong.
>
> – The plane leaves London at midday.
>
> – Ming arrives at Hong Kong airport at 10.30 am, Hong Kong time.
>
> – Ming's grandmother has three sisters.
>
> – The ticket costs £700.
>
> – Ming's grandmother is 72 years old.
>
> – The plane is 30 minutes late.
>
> – Ming's journey takes 14 hours.
>
> **What time is it in London when Ming arrives in Hong Kong?**

**Vocabulary**

24-hour clock

rearrange

reasoning

choose

decide

adjust

Discuss each statement and then give each pair of children a photocopy of the problem. Ask the children to cut out each statement, to discard the information they think is not relevant and to work out the answer to the question from the statements they have left. They should record their calculations so that others can read them.

**Key idea:** When you have a problem with lots of information, it helps to write each new idea on a separate piece of paper. You can then decide which information is irrelevant. You can put the information in a different order to help solve the problem.

### Plenary

The children present their solutions to the problem. Discuss with the children how they decided which information was relevant. Look at the order in which they dealt with the information.

### Homework

Give the children a copy of a world time chart to take home. Ask them to work out what time it is in different parts of the world when they are eating their breakfast.

## Multiplication and division

Is this always true, sometimes true or never true? Exploring general statements about multiplication and division will help children to formulate rules and reinforce their mental strategies.

### Starter

Challenge the children to respond rapidly to multiplication and division calculations involving one place of decimals:

– 6 multiplied by 0·7

– multiply 0·4 by 0·9

– divide 2·8 by 7

– 0·8 times 5

– 4·8 divided by 6

### Main activity

**Vocabulary**

product

multiple

prime

factor

Ask the children to test in groups some general statements about multiplication and division. Is the statement always, sometimes, or never true?

| | always true | sometimes true | never true |
|---|---|---|---|
| When dividing, the answer is smaller than the number you started with. | | ✓ | |
| Adding three consecutive numbers gives a multiple of 3. | | | |
| Multiples of 5 end in zero. | | | |
| All numbers have an even number of factors. | | | |
| Multiplying two odd numbers together gives you an odd number. | | | |
| All prime numbers are odd. | | | |

**Key idea:** You need to find just one example that does not work for a statement to prove that the statement cannot always be true.

### Plenary

Discuss with the children the difference between testing a statement and proving it. For example, no matter how many examples you use to show that the sum of three consecutive numbers is a multiple of 3, that does not prove the example.

### Homework

The quick way to multiply a single digit by 11 is just to write the digit down twice: 2 × 11 = 22. Can the children find a quick way to multiply a two-digit number by 11?

## Fractions, proportion and ratio

Providing realistic problems helps develop children's understanding of proportion and ratio. Work on making sense of situations rather than applying a formula.

### Starter

Put two different shapes on the board, such as:

Work on the different statements and questions that can be made from comparing the two shapes, such as:

– The larger shape is twice the area of the smaller shape

– The smaller shape is half the area of the larger shape

– There is one square in the smaller shape for every two in the larger shape

– If the larger shape was scaled up to 64 squares, what would be the area of the smaller shape?

### Main activity

**Vocabulary**

proportion

in every

for every

two in every three

two for every five

Work with the children on solving simple ratio and proportion problems in context:

– Sally wants to make carrot soup for eight people. How many onions will she need?

– Alan is making carrot soup for six people. How many carrots will he need?

– David has three onions to use up. If he makes carrot soup using all three onions, how much water will he need?

– Kate made carrot soup with 2·5 litres of water. How many carrots did she use?

> **Recipe**
>
> CARROT SOUP (serves 4)
> Ingredients:
> – 6 carrots
> – 2 onions
> – 4 medium potatoes
> – 1 litre of water
> – salt and pepper

**Key idea:** If we change one quantity we have to change others in the same ratio.

### Plenary

Ask the children to make up their own ratio and proportion problems to discuss and solve as a class: 'Gita shares out sixteen biscuits. She gives her baby brother one biscuit for every three biscuits she takes. How many biscuits does her brother get?'

### Homework

Give the children a piece of squared paper each. Ask them to design two patterns:

1. A pattern where three in every five squares are shaded

2. A pattern where three to every five squares are shaded.

Can the children explain in writing the differences in the numbers of squares shaded in each pattern?

# About the authors

Mike Askew is a lecturer at King's College, University of London, and a Director of BEAM Education. Originally trained as a primary school teacher, Mike taught in Inner and Outer London before moving into teacher training, first at Kingston Polytechnic and later at Thames Polytechnic.

Mike was appointed to King's College in 1990. He spends much of his time there researching the learning and teaching of primary mathematics. He has directed projects into Effective Teaching of Numeracy and Raising Attainment in Numeracy, and was part of the advisory group for the National Numeracy Project.

Currently he is deputy director of the five-year Leverhulme Numeracy Research project, which is investigating the progress in mathematical learning of some 3000 children across the primary age range.

Mike has written widely in the field of primary mathematics, and contributes to educational journals such as the Times Educational Supplement and Mathematics Teaching as well as Junior Education.

Sheila Ebbutt is the Managing Director of BEAM Education. She qualified as a teacher in 1974, and worked as a primary mathematics advisory teacher in Inner London for ten years. She spent time developing mathematics books and materials for teachers in Inner London schools.

Sheila was appointed to BEAM in September 1990. She directs all aspects of BEAM's activities, including writing, running courses, offering a range of consultancy and publishing teaching materials.

Sheila has written and contributed to many publications on mathematics education, including substantial resources for Scholastic Publication, Heinemann and Rigby, and articles in the professional press. She was part of the advisory group for the National Numeracy Project, and is a coordinator of the Early Childhood Mathematics Group.